Piper PA-28 Warrior
A Pilot's Guide

Piper PA-28 Warrior
A Pilot's Guide

Jeremy M Pratt

ISBN 1 874783 53 5

Airplan Flight Equipment

First Edition 1992
2nd Edition 2005

©Copyright 1992 Jeremy M Pratt and AFE Ltd.

Piper PA-28 Warrior
A Pilot's Guide
Jeremy M Pratt

ISBN 1 874783 53 5

Airplan Flight Equipment
1a Ringway Trading Estate
Shadowmoss Road
Manchester M22 5LH
Tel: 0161 499 0023
Fax: 0161 499 0298
www.afeonline.com

Contents

Authors Acknowledgments

I would like to thank all those whose knowledge, help and advice went into this book, in particular:

Airspeed Aviation

Air Nova

Simon Booth

CAA Safety Promotion Section

CSE Aviation

Colourmatch

Adrian Dickinson

Steve Dickinson

David Hockings

Andy Holland

Phil Huntington

Wendy Mellor

Manchester School of Flying

Margaret Parkes

Paul Price

Ravenair

Neil Rigby

John Ross

Ian Sixsmith

Louise Southern

Robert Taylor, GDi studio

John Thorpe

Cover image courtesy of Today's Pilot Magazine/Key Publishing

Sarah, Kate and Miles

Jeremy M Pratt

June 1993

General Description

General Description

▶The PA-28 Warrior

WARRIOR – a North American Indian experienced in battle.

The Warrior, described by Piper as the logical progression from the PA 28 Cherokee series, was first introduced in 1974. The most obvious difference is the re-designed, semi tapered wing, which contrasts strongly against the constant chord wing of the earlier models (known variously as the slab wing or plank wing for obvious reasons). This new wing gave handling, speed and payload advantages and in addition the cabin was bigger. In later years 'Velour' style interiors also became available as an option.

The Warrior I, in production from 1974 to 1977 is powered by a Lycoming 0-320 engine of 150HP, the Warrior II introduced in 1977 has an increased Maximum take-off Weight (MTOW) and a 160HP version of the 0-320 engine. The Cadet, essentially a stripped down trainer version of the Warrior II, was introduced in 1987.

The Archer II first built in 1976 features a 180HP engine, and a better payload capability than the Warrior to make it a good touring proposition. Both the Warrior and Archer were introduced to compete in a market dominated by the Cessna 172. They both offer certain advantages in the cabin comfort, but ultimately the buying decision often comes down to a simple preference for high or low wing aircraft. Since the Cessna 172 ceased production Piper have had, in theory, a virtual monopoly in the market for 4 seater touring aircraft. In fact many Warriors have become part of flying school fleets, and so the Cadet development. This book deals primarily with the Warrior II, with reference to the Cadet and Archer II where differences occur. Much of the information is also relevant to the Warrior I.

▶ Introduction

▶ Model Numbers and Production Years

▶ The Airframe

▶ The Flying Controls

▶ The Undercarriage

▶ The Engine

▶ The Propeller

▶ The Ignition System

▶ The Oil System

▶ The Starter System

▶ The Fuel System

▶ The Carburettor

▶ The Electrical System

▶ The Stall Warner System

▶ The Lighting System

▶ The Suction System

▶ The Pitot-Static System

▶ The Heating and Ventilation System

▶ Seats and Harnesses

▶ Doors and Windows

WARRIOR II
PA-28-161

PILOT'S
OPERATING
HANDBOOK

AND

FAA APPROVED
AIRPLANE FLIGHT MANUAL

AIRPLANE
SERIAL NO. _____ 28-8316077 _____ AIRPLANE
REGIST. NO. *G-BPWZ*

PA-28-161
REPORT: VB-1180 FAA APPROVED BY: *Ward Evans.*

WARD EVANS
D.O.A. NO. SO-1
DATE OF APPROVAL: PIPER AIRCRAFT CORPORATION
AUGUST 13, 1982   VERO BEACH, FLORIDA

"This is the flight manual which forms part of
Certificate of Airworthiness Number . *lkt.80*..."

FAA APPROVED IN NORMAL AND UTILITY CATEGORIES BASED ON CAR 3. THIS
HANDBOOK INCLUDES THE MATERIAL REQUIRED TO BE FURNISHED TO THE PILOT
BY CAR 3 AND CONSTITUTES THE APPROVED AIRPLANE FLIGHT MANUAL AND MUST
BE CARRIED IN THE AIRPLANE AT ALL TIMES.

The approved Pilot Operating Handbook/Flight Manual (illustrated above), as amended, is the only source of authoritative information. Each individual aircraft has its own individual POH/FM, in the interests of safety & good airmanship the pilot should be familiar with this document. This AFE Pilot Guide is not an authoritive document and should not be taken as such.

▶ Model Numbers and Production Years

PRODUCTION YEAR	MODEL	MODEL NAME

| 1974-1977 | PA-28-151 | Warrior |

| 1977-date | PA-28-161 | Warrior II |

| 1976-date | PA-28-181 | Archer II |

| 1987-date | PA-28-161 | Cadet |

The tail tie down point

▶The Airframe

The PA-28 airframe is generally described as being of all metal construction. The primary structure is constructed of aluminium alloy, with the engine mount being made from tubular steel. Some non-structural components such as the wing tips and undercarriage fairings are made from GRP.

The fuselage has a semi-monocoque structure, that is the vertical bulkheads and frames are joined by horizontal longerons and stringers which run the length of the fuselage. The metal skin is rivetted to the longerons and stringers, this arrangement is conventional for modern light aircraft and allows loads to be spread over the whole construction. At the rear of the fuselage the tail unit incorporates an 'all moving' tailplane, or stabilator. Underneath the rear fuselage a triangular combined tie down point and tail guard is fitted.

The wings are of cantilever design (unsupported by external struts or bracing) and have a positive dihedral. The wing is semi-tapered with a laminar flow aerofoil section. The wing main spars butt to a spar carry-through box which is an integral part of the fuselage structure. This structure runs under the rear seats and in effect provides a continuous main spar. On the upper surface of the right wing a black walkway is marked, this is the only area of the wing to be walked on or stood on. Underneath each wing a metal ring is fitted to be used as a tie down point.

The wing main spar at the wing root

The spar carry-through box, seen here on a disassembled Warrior

▶The Flying Controls

Dual flight controls are fitted as standard and link the cockpit controls to the control surface via cable linkages.

The AILERONS are of the differential type, moving upward through 25° and downward through 12.5° (1976 models on). A balance weight is fitted on a short rod at the outer end of each aileron, this weight is visible inside the wing tip cavity.

The FLAPS are of the simple slotted type, and manually operated from a lever between the cockpit seats and through a torque tube and push rods to the flap surfaces. Four positions can be selected, fully up (0°), 10°, 25° and 40°. The flaps lock in the fully up position, and only in this position can the walkway on the right hand flap be stood upon. In any other position the flaps will move rapidly down to 40° if any weight is placed on the right flap walkway, dumping the unwary onto the ground ! The button on the end of the flap lever is depressed to retract the flaps.

The RUDDER is operated from the rudder pedals (which are also linked to the steerable nose wheel) and can move through 27° either side of the neutral position. A rudder trimmer is fitted in the cockpit below the instrument panel. This wheel is spring loaded to trim out excessive rudder forces in flight. The rudder trim control turns clockwise to give nose right trim and anti-clockwise to give nose left trim. As the rudder is connected (via rods from the rudder pedals) to the nose wheel the control surface cannot be moved whilst the aircraft is stationary without exerting considerable force – this is not recommended.

The Warrior has an all moving STABILATOR, which functions as a combined tailplane and elevator, it moves up 14° from neutral and down 2° from neutral. The control functions in the natural sense, and by design provides a very powerful pitching force. As part of its design the stabilator incorporates an ANTI-BALANCE TAB at its trailing edge, sometimes referred to as an anti-servo tab. This tab combines two functions. It moves in the same direction as the stabilator to provide a 'damping' force, increasing the feel of the control, very important with such a powerful control surface. In addition the anti-balance tab acts

as a trimmer to trim out pitching forces on the control wheel, the control surface moves 3° up from neutral and 12° down from neutral. The cockpit control for the trimmer is a conventional trim wheel located on the cockpit floor between the seats, and acts in the normal sense, rotating the wheel forwards to trim nose down and backwards to trim nose up.

The all moving stabilator and anti balance tab

Do not step on the flap walkway if the flaps are in the down position

A fully faired main undercarriage

▶The Undercarriage

The Warrior UNDERCARRIAGE is fixed and of the tricycle type, the main undercarriage has a track of 10'.

The main undercarriage legs incorporate an air-oil oleo strut to absorb operating loads, normally the main gear struts should have about 4.5 inches of the piston tube exposed under normal static load (aircraft with full fuel and oil). The Warrior I and first year (1977) Warrior II's have standard wheel fairings on the main and nose wheels. From 1978 models on the main and nose undercarriage legs have a full fairing, which joins the wheel fairings. The Cadet has no wheel or undercarriage leg fairings. The main undercarriage is fitted with 6.00 x 6 wheels.

The nose gear attaches to the engine mount and also has an air/oil oleo strut to damp and absorb the normal operating loads, normally about 3.25 inches of the piston tube should be exposed. On the rear of the nose leg a torque link fitted to maintain the correct alignment of the nose wheel, its lower arm is fitted to the nose wheel fork and the upper arm to the oleo cylinder casing. The nose gear is steerable through direct linkage to the rudder pedals, a spring device aids nose wheel and rudder centering, and is also adjustable to act as the rudder trim (see rudder). Bungee springs are incorporated in the nose wheel steering mechanism to aid lighter and smoother nose wheel steering.

The nose wheel has a range of movement of 30° either side of dead ahead (20° on the Cadet).

The nose wheel tyre is a 5.00 x 5 unit, on the Warrior, and a 6.00 x 6 unit on the Archer II.

In common with just about all light aircraft the nose leg is not as strong as the main gear, a point that will be covered in more detail later in this book.

The brake fluid reservoir on the upper left firewall

A faired nosewheel assembly

The BRAKE system consists of single disc brake assemblies fitted to each main wheel and operated by a hydraulic system. The brake lever located below the centre of the instrument panel operates a master cylinder located below and behind the control panel. When the control is pulled back braking is evenly applied to both main wheels. A small button on the side of the brake lever allows it to be locked in the On position to act as a parking brake. To release the parking brake the control is pulled back (which unlatches the button), and then pushed fully forward. When toe brakes are fitted, they are operated by depressing the upper half of the rudder pedal. In this system each toe brake has a separate brake cylinder above the pedal, and it is possible to operate the brakes differentially – to the left or right wheel. This system allows the aircraft to turn in a very tight circle, and it is possible to lock one main wheel with the use of some pedal force.Turning around a wheel in this fashion tends to 'scrub' the tyre and is generally discouraged. A brake fluid reservoir which feeds to all the brake cylinders is fitted to the upper left forward face of the firewall (accessed via the left engine cowling). Here it can be inspected for fluid level and replenished if necessary.

▶The Engine

The Warrior I (1974 – 1977) is fitted with a Lycoming 0-320-E engine of 150HP at 2700 RPM. The Warrior II (including CADET) has a Lycoming 0-320-D engine giving 160HP at 2700 RPM. The Archer II has a Lycoming 0-360-A engine of 180HP at 2700 RPM. The 320 and 360 designators refer to the cubic capacity of the engine in inches. Apart from this difference the engine models are similar and are treated as one in the following section.

The engine is a four cylinder unit, with cylinders horizontally opposed across the crankshaft. The cylinders are staggered so that each connecting rod has its own crankshaft throw, the cylinders are steel barrels with aluminium alloy cylinder heads screwed on with interference fits.

The engine is air cooled. Airflow enters the engine compartment at the front of the cowling, and is directed by baffles to flow over the whole engine. The cylinders feature deep cooling fins to aid cooling, the airflow leaves the engine compartment at the rear lower cowling underneath the engine compartment.

The engine is mounted on a steel tubular mounting which attaches to the firewall.

Latching the cowling, note the top of the latch is under the tab on the cowling.

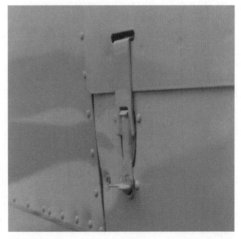

Cowling latch properly closed and locked with a half turn of the catch

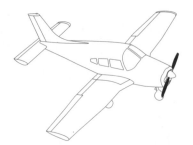

▶The Propeller

The propeller is an all metal, two bladed, fixed pitch design, turned by direct drive from the engine crankshaft, the propeller rotates clockwise as seen from the cockpit. For the Warrior II and Cadet the diameter is 74", The Archer II propeller has a diameter of 76".

▶The Ignition System

The engine features a dual ignition system, fitted with two magnetos. The magnetos are small AC generators which are driven by the crankshaft rotation to provide a very high voltage to a distributor, which directs it via high voltage leads (or high tension leads) to the spark plugs. At the spark plug the current must cross a gap, in doing so a spark is produced which ignites the fuel/air mixture in the cylinder.

The magnetos are fitted at the rear of the engine, one each side of the engine centre line (hence Left and Right magnetos). The usual arrangement is for each magneto to fire the bottom spark plugs of the two cylinders on one side of the engine and the top spark plugs on the other side. Each cylinder has two spark plugs (top and bottom) for safety and efficiency. The leads that run from the magnetos to the spark plugs should be secure and there should be no splits or cracks in the plastic insulation covering the leads.

It is worth emphasising that the ignition system is totally independent of the aircraft electrical system, and once the engine is running it will operate regardless of the serviceability of the battery or alternator.

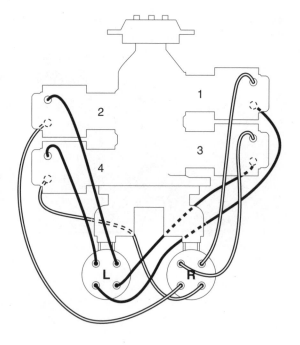

▶The Oil System

The oil system of the engine provides for lubrication, cooling, sealing, cleansing and protection against corrosion. The system is a wet – sump, pressure feed system. The oil sump is located under the engine, and oil is drawn from here by the engine driven oil pump and through a cooler and filter and into the oil gallery of the right half of the crankcase. When the oil has flowed around the engine it drains down to the sump by gravity. An oil pressure relief valve is fitted in upper right side of the crankcase. The function of this valve is to maintain the correct operating pressure over a wide range of temperatures and RPM settings. Above a certain pressure the valve will open and allow oil to return to the sump rather than continuing into the lubricating system.

Oil contents can be checked on a dip stick which is accessible from the right hand side of the engine. The dipstick is graduated in US quarts and measures the contents of the oil sump. When the engine has been running, the oil will take up to 10 minutes to return to the sump, and only then can a true reading be taken. When replacing the dipstick care must be taken not too over-tighten the cap. To do so may make it exceptionally difficult to open the cap again, and it is quite possible to strip the thread on the cap or filler pipe.

Oil filler pipe

The oil temperature gauge and oil pressure gauge in the cockpit enable the pilot to monitor the health of the oil system.

The Warriors and Archers (excepting the 1974 Warrior I Models) are fitted with an annunciator panel at the top centre of the instrument panel below the compass. This panel has three warning lights for VAC (vacuum), OIL (oil pressure) and ALT (electrical system). A test button is fitted to check the operation of the lights when the engine is running. The OIL warning light illuminates if oil pressure falls below 35psi.

The warning annunciator panel

▶The Starter System

The starter motor is housed at the lower front left side of the engine. It incorporates a geared cog that engages on to the teeth of the starter ring when the starter is operated. As the engine is turned an impulse coupling in the left magneto operates, this retards the spark and aids starting. When the engine fires and begins to rotate under its own power this impulse coupling ceases to operate and normal spark timing is resumed. When the key is released, allowing the key to return to the 'BOTH' position, the cog on the starter motor withdraws at a predetermined engine RPM to be clear of the starter ring.

A STARTER WARNING LIGHT is fitted in the cockpit. This illuminates when the starter is operated to show that the starter motor is engaging the starter ring. When the key is released the light should go out. If the light remains on this means that the starter motor is still engaged with the starter ring. In this instance the starter motor will be turned by the engine, and serious damage may be caused to the aircraft electrical system. If the starter warning light remains lit once the engine is running the engine should be shut down without delay.

▶The Fuel System

The Warrior has two aluminium fuel tanks, located in the inboard leading edge of each wing. From these tanks a fuel line runs through the wing and fuselage to the fuel selector valve located on the left lower cockpit wall in the pilot footwell. From this valve the fuel line runs through the firewall to a fuel strainer bowl mounted on the forward left face of the firewall. From the strainer bowl a fuel line runs through the electric fuel pump and engine driven fuel pump to the carburettor. A separate line runs from the strainer bowl to the cockpit primer and from there to three cylinders.

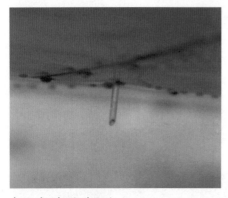

Two TANK VENTS, one for each fuel tank, protrude from the lower surface of each wing. The forward facing pipe vent ensures that ambient pressure is maintained above the fuel in the fuel tank. Should this vent become blocked a vacuum may form in the tank as the fuel level lowers, and fuel flow to the engine may be interrupted.

There are three FUEL STRAINERS (or quick drains), one at the lower rear inboard edge of each tank, accessible from the inboard lower wing surface, and one from the fuel bowl, accessed at the lower left cowling. Fuel can only be drawn from the bowl if the cockpit fuel selector is in the Left or Right position.

An underwing tank vent

An underwing fuel strainer

The engine fuel strainer with warning sign

The shape of the fuel strainers has been the cause of problems. To take a fuel sample the bar of the strainer is pushed up against a spring, and fuel will flow into the fuel tester. When the bar is released it should return to its original position, and the fuel flow ceases.

The original strainer has a 'lip', which makes it possible for the valve to lock in the open position, and fuel to continue to drain through the valve even after the bar has been released. If this occurs to the tank strainers the result will be the loss of fuel from the tanks, and possible fuel exhaustion.

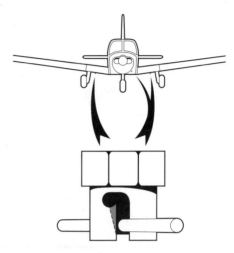

If the engine fuel strainer is open, the likely result is engine failure just after take-off due to fuel starvation. In documented incidents where the fuel was NOT turned on for the fuel drain check, the fact that the engine fuel strainer was locked open was missed. The start, taxy, power checks and take-off were normal, however the engine failed just after take-off.

A recommended modification is for operators to file off an area of the strainer valve so that the bar cannot lock in the open position. Obviously, whether or not this modification has been carried out care should be exercised when operating the fuel drains.

The cockpit FUEL SELECTOR can also be problematical. The selector is located on the lower left cockpit wall of the pilot's footwell, and so is not easily accessible to a pilot (say an instructor) in the right seat. Also with the selector being somewhat out of sight particular care should be exercised when moving the selector lever. The selector can be used to feed the engine from either the Left or Right tank. To turn the fuel Off a spring loaded latch on the selector must first be depressed and then the lever rotated to the Off position. This operation can be a two handed operation, which does help prevent the accidental selection of the Off position.

The cockpit fuel selector (selected "OFF")

In normal operation the fuel is drawn through the system by an engine driven FUEL PUMP. However should this pump fail the fuel supply to the carburettor will cease and the engine will stop. Therefore a second, electrical fuel pump is fitted, this pump is selected On or Off from a cockpit switch. Normally the electric fuel pump is used during take-off and landing, and when changing tanks. A fuel pressure gauge is fitted, reading from a sender between the engine driven fuel pump and the carburettor.

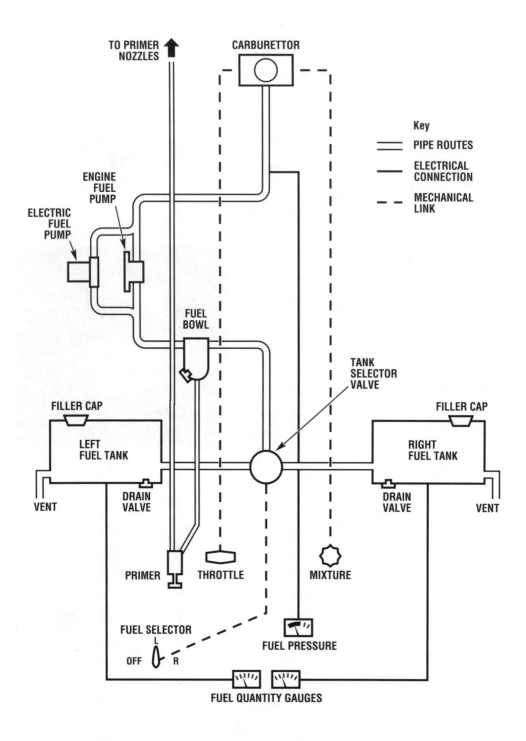

▶The Carburettor

The carburettor mixes air with the fuel from the fuel system and supplies the fuel/air mix to the cylinders. The carburettor is located under the engine, and takes induction air from a scoop intake in the lower front cowling. This air is filtered and then fed into the carburettor air box. In this box a butterfly valve is used to allow either the filtered air, or heated air, to be fed to the carburettor. Heated air comes from an unfiltered inlet inside the front cowling which then passes into a shroud around the exhaust which heats it before it reaches the carburettor. Hot or cold air is selected via the carburettor heat control in the cockpit, the use of this control and the subject of carburettor icing are fully fully discussed later in this book.

From the carburettor the fuel/air mix is carried to the induction manifold and to the inlet port of each cylinder.

The carburettor is fitted with an ACCELERATOR PUMP. With a normal carburettor sudden opening of the throttle can cause the engine to falter, due to an excessively lean mixture, a 'lean mixture cut'. The accelerator pump introduces a charge of fuel when the throttle is suddenly opened to cure this problem. However if the throttle is opened too quickly (say in under 2 seconds) the extra fuel can cause a 'rich mixture cut'.

The PRIMER CONTROL situated next to the throttle quadrant is an aid to starting. The control is unlocked by rotating it until a pin on the shaft aligns with the cut out in the collar. The control can then be pulled out, filling the primer with fuel from the fuel bowl. The primer is then pushed in, delivering fuel to the cylinder intake ports. For a cold engine three cycles of the primer is usually sufficient. When priming is completed the primer should be pushed fully in with the pin aligned with the collar cut out, and then rotated about half a turn to lock the primer. As a check attempt to pull the primer out, it should remain locked. It is important that the primer is fully locked, otherwise engine rough running may result.

The MIXTURE is controlled from the mixture lever located in the cockpit which adjusts the fuel/air ratio in the carburettor. The use of this control is fully covered later in the book, however in the fully forward position it gives a RICH mixture, and if moved to the rearward ICO (Idle Cut Off) position the fuel supply is cut off and the engine stops.

The power quadrant has a lever on its right side. Movement of this 'friction' control adjusts the friction of the throttle and mixture levers, and allows for them to be kept in the desired position. Generally this lever is adjusted to leave the throttle and mixture with relatively loose and easy movement on the ground, but is tightened to hold the levers in position for take-off.

▶The Electrical System

The Warrior has a 14 volt, direct current electrical system. The alternator is mounted to the front lower right of the engine and is engine driven from a belt drive off a pulley directly behind the starter ring. The alternator is rated at 60 amps, a 12 volt battery is located inside a thermo-plastic box under the rear seat on the right hand side, or on the right forward face of the firewall from 1983 models on. On the Archer aircraft the battery is located aft of the baggage compartment.

The ALTERNATOR is the primary source of power to the electrical system in normal operations with the engine running. The alternator produces alternating current (AC) which is converted into direct current (DC) by diodes incorporated in the alternator housing which act as rectifiers. By their design alternators require a small voltage (about 3 volts) to produce the electromagnetic field required inside the alternator. The significance of this is that if the battery is completely discharged (flat), the alternator will not be able to supply any power to the electrical system, even after the engine has been started by some other means (ie external power or hand swinging). Output from the alternator is controlled by a VOLTAGE REGULATOR which is mounted behind the left hand side of the instrument panel. An OVERVOLTAGE RELAY protects the system from possible damage due to an overvoltage condition. In the event of an over-voltage (over approx 16.5 volts) the relay opens and the alternator can be assumed to have failed.

The primary purpose of the BATTERY is to provide power for engine starting, the initial excitation of the alternator and as a backup in the event of alternator failure. In normal operations with the engine running the alternator provides the power to the electrical system and charges the battery. A fully charged battery has a charging rate of about 2 amperes, in a partially discharged condition (ie just after engine start) the charging rate can be much higher than this. In the event of an alternator failure the battery provides ALL power to the electrical system. In theory a fully charged 35 ampere hour battery is capable of providing 35 amps for 1 hour, or 1 amp for 35 hours, or 17.5 amps for 2 hours etc. In practice the power available is governed by factors such as battery age and condition, load placed on it etc. The best advice is to reduce electrical load to the minimum consistent with safety, and plan to make a landing at the earliest opportunity.

The AMMETER, located in the engine instrument group, indicates in amperes the electrical load on the alternator. With the engine running and all electrical services turned off, the ammeter will indicate the charging rate of the battery. As services are switched on the ammeter will indicate the additional load of each item. In the case of night flight the maximum continuous load will be in the region of 30 amps. In the event of alternator failure the ammeter will indicate zero, and where fitted a red 'Low Voltage' warning light will illuminate. Except for some early Warrior I's an ANNUNCIATOR PANEL is fitted in the upper instrument panel (previously described in the oil system section). The ALT warning light of the annunciator panel will illuminate if the alternator fails.

EXTERNAL POWER

The external power receptacle

The pilot controls the electrical system via the 'MASTER SWITCH' located on instrument panel at the left end of the electrical rocker switch group. This switch is a split rocker switch having two halves, labelled 'BAT' and 'ALT', and normally the switch is operated as one, both halves being used together. The 'BAT' half of the switch can be operated independently, so that all electrical power is being drawn from the battery only; however the 'ALT' side can only be turned on in conjunction with the 'BAT' half. Should an electrical problem occur the MASTER Switch can be used to reset the electrical system by turning it OFF for 2 seconds and then turning it ON again.

The aircraft may be fitted with an EXTERNAL POWER RECEPTACLE and the right hand fuselage aft of the wing root, this can be used to connect external power for starting or operation of the aircraft electrical system. Before using external power it is imperative to check that the external power unit is of the correct voltage – otherwise SERIOUS DAMAGE COULD BE INFLICTED ON THE ELECTRICAL SYSTEM. Additionally it should be remembered that if the battery is totally flat (completely discharged), it will need to be removed and recharged or replaced before flight.

To use external power the following procedure should be adopted:

1. Check that MASTER SWITCH and all ELECTRICAL EQUIPMENT is OFF

2. Ensure that the RED lead of the jumper cable goes to POSITIVE (+) terminal of the external power source and the BLACK lead to the NEGATIVE (-).

3. Insert the cable plug into the aircraft EXTERNAL POWER RECEPTACLE socket.

4. Turn the MASTER SWITCH ON, and proceed with normal starting procedure.

5. After engine start turn MASTER SWITCH and all ELECTRICAL EQUIPMENT OFF and remove the cable plug from the aircraft.

6. Turn the MASTER SWITCH ON, and check the ammeter. If no output is shown flight should not attempted.

The various electrically operated systems are protected by individual CIRCUIT BREAKERS, which are located on the lower instrument panel. Should a problem (eg a short circuit) occur the relevant circuit breaker may 'pop', and will be seen to be raised in relation to the other circuit breakers (CBs). The correct procedure is to allow the CB to cool for say 2 minutes, then reset it and check the result. If the CB pops again it should not be reset.

Apart from engine starting and the alternator field the electrical system supplies power to the following:

ALL internal and external lights.

ALL radios and intercom.

Turn Coordinator, Fuel Gauges, Oil temperature Gauge, Annunciator Panel.

Stall Warner, Pitot Heater, Electric Fuel Pump.

▶The Stall Warner System

A horn is electrically activated from a stall warning vane on the leading edge of the left wing. This vane moves up at angles of attack approaching the stall, and gives a warning at approx 5 to 10 knots above the stall speed.

The wing mounted stall warner vane

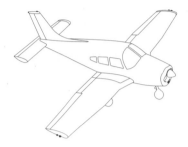

▶The Lighting System

The Warrior may be equipped with a variety of optional internal and external lighting. Where wingtip 'Strobe' lights are fitted care should be used in their operation. As a general rule the strobes are not used during taxying as they can dazzle and distract those nearby, they are however very effective in the air. If flying in cloud conditions or heavy precipitation it is recommended that they be turned off as the pilot may become spatially disoriented. The landing light is fitted in the lower front nose cowling, again it should be used with some discretion, not least because of the very short life of the lamp bulbs.

The wing tip navigation light and strobe light unit

▶The Suction System

An engine driven vacuum pump is mounted to the upper rear face of the engine. This pump is fitted with a plastic shear drive, so that should the pump seize, the shear drive will fail and the engine will not be damaged. The air enters the suction system through a filter, passes through the air driven gyro instruments (and is measured by the suction gauge), into the vacuum regulator and on to the vacuum pump, from which it is expelled through a short pipe.

Suction is used to drive the gyros in the Attitude Indicator (or Artificial Horizon) and Heading Indicator (or Direction Indicator). A suction gauge mounted on the instrument panel measures suction, for cruising RPMs and altitudes the reading should be 5.0, within 0.1 inches of mercury. A lower suction over an extended period may indicate a faulty vacuum regulator, dirty screens or a system leak. If the vacuum pump fails or a line collapses the suction gauge reading will fall to zero, and the Attitude Indicator and Heading Indicator will become unreliable over a period of some minutes as the gyros run down losing RPM. The real danger here is that the effect is gradual and may not be noticed by the pilot for some time.

The Suction System

▶The Pitot-Static System

The pitot static system supplies static pressure to the Vertical Speed Indicator (VSI) and Altimeter and pitot and static pressure to the Airspeed Indicator (ASI).

Pitot and static pressure comes from a PRESSURE HEAD which is located under the left wing. No checking system is incorporated in the system, and instrument indications in the event of a leak or blockage are outside of the scope of this book. As an option the pitot head has a heating element which is activated by a switch in the electrical rocker switch group on the instrument panel, labelled 'PITOT HEAT'. Pitot heat can prevent blockage of the pitot head in heavy rain or icing, this not withstanding it must be remembered that the PA-28 IS NOT CLEARED FOR FLIGHT INTO KNOWN ICING CONDITIONS. Should the static lines become blocked, an alternate static source is available as an option, the control valve is located under the left instrument panel. When this valve is operated cabin air feeds the static system, the DV window and cabin vents should be closed, and the cabin heater and defrost turned on. A drain valve that serves both the pitot and static lines is located on the lower left cabin wall.

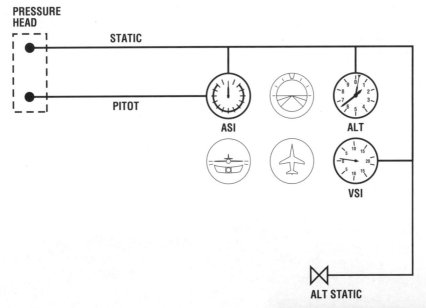

The pressure head should be checked before flight to ensure that the pitot and static ports are unobstructed, the pressure head which may be protected on the ground with a removable pitot cover. It is important not to blow into either pitot or static vents, doing so can result in damage to the pressure instruments.

The pressure head

▶The Heating and Ventilation System

Cabin heating is supplied via a shroud around the engine exhaust system. This allows air which has entered from an inlet in the rear engine baffles inside the cowling to be warmed by the exhaust pipes, it can then be directed to outlets between the front seats (cabin heat) or at the lower windscreen (defrost) by two levers mounted at the far right instrument panel. The system is very effective once the engine is warm, although its use is governed by a couple of safety factors.

Firstly the heating system effectively opens a path through the firewall between the engine compartment and the cockpit. For this reason the cabin heat and defrost are selected OFF before engine start, or if fire is suspected in the engine compartment.

Secondly with a system of this type there is a danger of Carbon Monoxide (CO) being introduced into the cabin. Carbon Monoxide is a gas produced as a by product of the combustion process. It is colourless, odourless and tasteless, but its effects are potentially fatal, the dangers of Carbon Monoxide are widely publicised. A generally accepted practice is to shut off the heating system if engine fumes (which may contain CO) are thought to be entering the cockpit. The danger arises if a crack or split is present in the exhaust system inside the heating shroud allowing carbon monoxide to enter the heating system.

The ventilation system consists of cockpit vents, individually controllable, directing fresh air to just ahead of each seat, the inlets for this air are in the inner leading edge of each wing. In addition an overhead ventilation system may be fitted. This system takes fresh air from an inlet in the leading edge of the fin to vents in the cabin ceiling. An electrically powered blower may be fitted to the overhead ventilation system to boost air through this system when on the ground. When the heating system is in use it is recommended that the fresh air vents be operated to give a comfortable temperature mix. Doing so will help to combat the possible danger of carbon monoxide poisoning, and on a more mundane level will stop the cabin becoming 'stuffy' and possibly inducing drowsiness in the pilot.

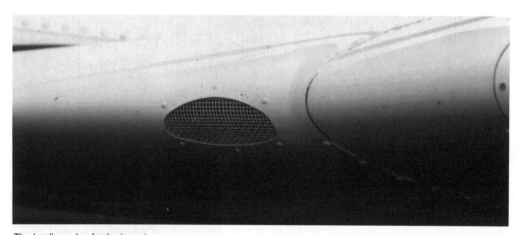

The leading edge fresh air vent

▶ Seats and Harnesses

The front seats are adjustable fore and aft. The bar which unlocks the seat position is located below the forward edge of the seat cushion. This bar is raised and then the seat can be moved fore and aft. When the desired position is reached the bar is released and the pilot should check that the seat is positively locked in position. As an option the front seats may also be adjustable for height. Generally entry to and exit from the front seats is easiest with the seats in the rearmost position. When the seats are unoccupied the seat backs can be tilted forward to allow access to the rear seats. To get to the rear seats the front seats are best in the fully forward position. The Cadet may have a rear 'bench' seat fitted as an option.

Harness design may vary between different aircraft. In addition to the lap strap, a single inertia reel shoulder strap is fitted and their use should be considered mandatory, as upper torso restraint has been shown to be a major factor in accident survivability. The inertia reel can be checked by pulling sharply on the shoulder strap, the reel should lock and prevent the strap from extending further.

The baggage area behind the rear seats is fitted with restraint straps for the securing of items placed in this area. For the Warrior and Archer maximum baggage to be carried in this area is 200lbs (90kg), evenly distributed. For the Cadet the maximum baggage is 50lbs (22kg). Attention should be drawn to the weight and balance implications of weight in this area, it also must be remembered that for some manoeuvres the carriage of baggage is prohibited.

The rear baggage door

▶ Doors And Windows

.The PA-28 has a single door on the right hand side of the cabin to allow for access to the cabin via the right wing walkway.

The design of the door latches varies according to the model year of the particular aircraft. On Warriors pre 1976 the cabin door has a simple 'pull to open' latch ahead of the door armrest. This is supplemented by a latch on the upper portion of the door. From inside the lever is rotated rearwards to latch the door, the inward movement of the upper part of the door normally makes it clear that the latch has engaged. On 1976 models and on the overhead latch operates in the same fashion, but the latch ahead on the door armrest is moved down to aid door latching.

The top door latch and lever

The lower door locking lever

Although it is important for the door to be properly latched for flight, the consequences of partial door opening in flight are usually not serious. In fact the door can usually be closed by slowing to about 87 knots IAS, with the DV window open and the cabin vents closed. The offending latch can then be operated, whilst pulling on the door if necessary.

IMPORTANT: Where accidents do occur after a door opening in-flight, they are often caused by pilot distraction from the primary task of flying the aeroplane, rather than as a direct result of the open door.

When entering and leaving the cabin, the top of the door should not be used as a hand grip to support body weight, as damage to the door and door hinges may result.

A separate BAGGAGE DOOR is fitted to the right side of the Warrior and Archer models (but not the Cadet) to allow easy access to the baggage area. It is important to check that this door is properly closed and latched before flight.

The 'DV' window

An inward opening 'DV WINDOW' is fitted to the left hand window. This window can be opened in flight where visibility through the windscreen has been impaired, or to aid ventilation.

The aircraft design and window area gives the aircraft reasonable forward and side visibility. This visibility can be degraded by oil smears, insects and other matter accumulating on the windows. For window cleaning a soft cloth and warm soapy water is recommended, to remove oil and grease a cloth soaked in kerosene can be used. The use of petrol, alcohol, thinners and window cleaner sprays is not recommended.

Limitations

Limitations

▶ PA-28 161 Warrior and PA-28 181 Archer Dimensions

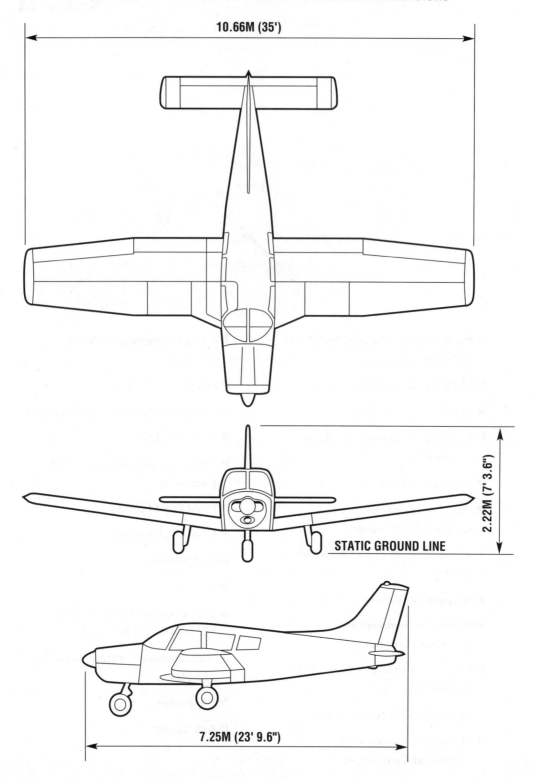

10.66M (35')

2.22M (7' 3.6")

STATIC GROUND LINE

7.25M (23' 9.6")

▶PA-28 161 Cadet Dimensions

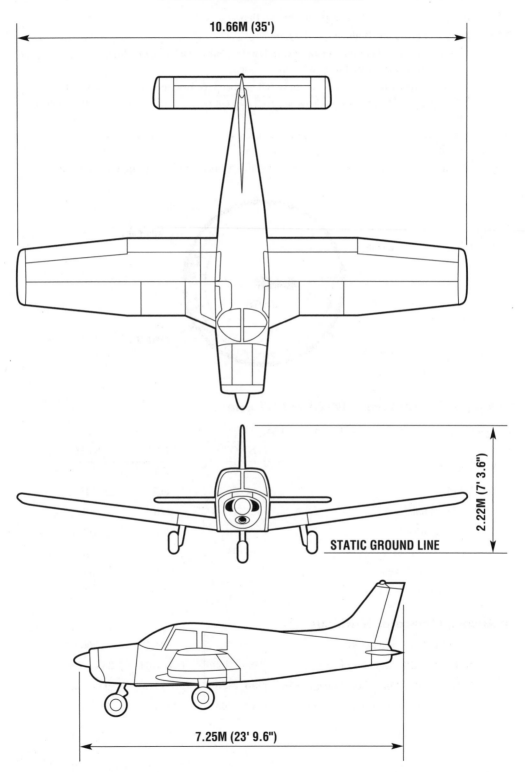

10.66M (35')

2.22M (7' 3.6")

STATIC GROUND LINE

7.25M (23' 9.6")

▶The 'V' Airspeed Code

VS0   (Bottom of white arc) Stalling speed with full flap.

VS1   (Bottom of green arc) Stalling speed 0 flap.

VFE   (Top of white arc) Maximum airspeed with flaps extended. Do not extend flaps above this speed, or fly faster than this speed with any flap extended.

VA   Design manoeuvring speed. Do not make full or abrupt control movements when flying faster than this speed. Design manoeuvring speed should not be exceeded when flying in turbulent conditions.

VNO   (Top of green arc) Maximum structural cruising speed. Do not exceed this speed except in smooth air conditions.

VNE   (Red line) Never exceed speed. Do not exceed this airspeed under any circumstances.

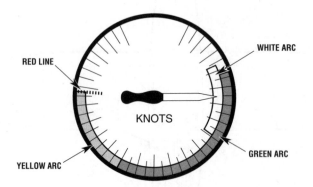

▶Airspeed Limitations – PA-28 161 (Warrior II)

(all quoted speeds are INDICATED airspeed – IAS)

	KNOTS	MPH	KPH
VNE	160	184	296
VNO	126	145	233
VA (at 2440lbs)	111	128	206
VA (at 1531lbs)	88	101	163
VFE	103	118	191
Stalling Speed clean	50	58	93
Stalling Speed Full Flap	44	51	81

▶Airspeed Indicator Markings

	KNOTS	MPH	KPH
RED LINE (Never Exceed)	160	184	296
YELLOW ARC (Caution range)	126 – 160	145 – 184	233 – 296
GREEN ARC (Normal operating range)	50 – 126	58 – 145	93 – 233
WHITE ARC (Flap extended range)	44 – 103	51 – 118	81 – 191

▶ Maximum Demonstrated Crosswind Component

17 Knots

▶ Airspeed Limitations – PA-28 161 (Cadet)

(quoted speeds are INDICATED airspeed – IAS)

	KNOTS	MPH	KPH
VNE	160	184	296
VNO	126	145	233
VA (at 2325lbs)	111	128	206
VA (at 1531lbs)	88	101	163
VFE	103	118	191
Stalling Speed clean	50	58	93
Stalling Speed Full Flap	44	51	81

▶ Airspeed Indicator Markings

	KNOTS	MPH	KPH
RED LINE (Never Exceed)	160	184	296
YELLOW ARC (Caution range)	126-160	145-184	233-296
GREEN ARC (Normal operating range)	50-126	58-145	93-233
WHITE ARC (Flap extended range)	44-103	51-118	81-191

▶ Maximum Demonstrated Crosswind Component

17 Knots

▶ Airspeed Limitations – PA-28 181 (Archer II)

(INDICATED airspeed – IAS)

	KNOTS	MPH	KPH
VNE	154	177	285
VNO	125	144	232
VA (at 2550lbs)	113	130	209
VA (at 1634lbs)	89	102	165
VFE	102	117	189
Stalling Speed clean	55	63	102
Stalling Speed Full Flap	49	56	91

▶Airspeed Indicator Markings

(INDICATED airspeed – IAS)

	KNOTS	MPH	KPH
RED LINE (Never Exceed)	154	177	285
YELLOW ARC (Caution range)	125-154	144-177	232-285
GREEN ARC (Normal operating range)	55-125	63-144	102-232
WHITE ARC (Flap extended range)	49-102	56-117	91-189

▶Maximum Demonstrated Crosswind Component

17 Knots

▶Airframe Limitations PA-28 161 (Warrior II)

WEIGHTS	NORMAL		UTILITY	
	lbs	Kg	lbs	Kg
Maximum Take-off Weight	2440	1107	2020	916
Maximum Landing Weight	2440	1107	2020	916
Maximum Baggage Weight	200	90	0	0

▶Flight Load Factors

	NORMAL	UTILITY
Max Positive load factor:	3.8G	4.4G

Max Negative load factor: NO INVERTED MANOEUVRES PERMITTED

Some Warrior II aircraft may be certified at a reduced weight.

WEIGHTS	NORMAL		UTILITY	
	lbs	Kg	lbs	Kg
Maximum Take-off Weight	2325	1054	2020	916
Maximum Landing Weight	2325	1054	2020	916
Maximum Baggage Weight	200	90	0	0

Check the POH/FM for the actual aircraft you are using to confirm the correct limitations.

▶Airframe Limitations PA-28 161 (Cadet)

WEIGHTS	NORMAL		UTILITY	
	lbs	Kg	lbs	Kg
Maximum Take-off Weight	2325	1054	2020	916
Maximum Landing Weight	2325	1054	2020	916
Maximum Baggage Weight	50	22	0	0

▶ Flight Load Factors

	NORMAL	UTILITY
Max Positive load factor:	3.8G	4.4G
Max Negative load factor:	NO INVERTED MANOEUVRES PERMITTED	

▶ Airframe Limitations PA-28 181 (Archer II)

WEIGHTS	NORMAL		UTILITY	
	lbs	Kg	lbs	Kg
Maximum Take-off Weight	2550	1156	2130	966
Maximum Landing Weight	2550	1156	2130	966
Maximum Baggage Weight	200	90	0	0

▶ Flight Load Factors

	NORMAL	UTILITY
Max Positive load factor:	3.8G	4.4G
Max Negative load factor:	NO INVERTED MANOEUVRES PERMITTED	

▶ Engine Limitations

	Tachometer	Instrument Marking
Maximum RPM	2700	Red Line
Normal Operating Range	500-2700	Green Arc

	Oil Temperature	Instrument Marking
Normal operating range	75-245°F	Green Arc
Maximum	245°F	Red Line

	Oil Pressure	Instrument Marking
Normal operating range	60-90psi	Green Arc
Minimum	25psi	Red Line
Maximum	100psi (1)	Red Line
Caution range – idle	25-60psi	Yellow Arc
Caution range – warm up (2)	90-100psi	Yellow Arc

(1) 90psi for Archer II

(2) Warrior II only

▶ Oil Quantity

Note: dipstick is marked in US quarts

	US quart	Litre
Capacity	8	7.57
Minimum safe quantity	2	1.9

(+1 quart per hour planned flight)

▶ Fuel System

Fuel Quantity *Note: cockpit fuel gauges are marked in US gallons*

	US Gal	Imp Gal	Litre
Total Capacity	50	41.6	189.3
Unuseable Fuel	2	1.6	7.6
Usable Fuel	48	40	181.7
Indicator Tab	34 (17 per tank)	28.3	128.7

Fuel Pressure	Gauge Indication	
Maximum	8.0psi	Red Line
Minimum	0.5psi	Red Line
Normal operating range	0.5-8.0psi	Green Arc

▶ Miscellaneous Limitations PA-28 161 (Warrior II & Cadet)

Nose Wheel Tyre Pressure	30psi	2.1 Bar
Main Wheel Tyre Pressure	24psi	1.7 Bar

▶ Miscellaneous Limitations PA-28 181 (Archer II)

Nose Wheel Tyre Pressure	18psi	1.2 Bar
Main Wheel Tyre Pressure	24psi	1.7 Bar

▶ Oil Grades

Lycoming approve lubricating oil for the engine that conforms to specification MIL-L-6082 (straight mineral type) and specification MIL-L-22851 (ashless dispersant type).

Straight mineral type – known mostly as straight oil – is usually only used when the engine is new, or after maintenance work on the engine. Straight oil grades are known by their number – ie 80, 100.

Ashless dispersant oils are more commonly used in service. These oil grades carry the prefix 'W', ie W80, W100. Ashless dispersant type – 'W' oil – must not be used where the engine is operating on straight oil, nor can 'W' oil be added to straight mineral oil. It is therefore very important to check which type of oil is currently being used in the engine and be sure to only add the same type.

Both types of oil are available in different grades, used according to the average surface air temperature. The recommended grades are set out as SAE numbers, but available in commercial grade numbers – which are different! The situation is more simple than it appears, to get the approximate commercial grade, double the SAE number, ie SAE 50 = commercial grade 100 (or W100). The tables show the recommended grades for various surface temperature bands.

AVERAGE AIR TEMPERATURE	MIL-L-6082 Straight mineral	COMMERCIAL GRADE
Above 60°F/16°C	SAE 50	100
30°F/-1°C-90°F/32°C	SAE 40	80
0°F/-18°C-70°F/21°C	SAE 30	65
Below 10°F/-12°C	SAE 20	55
AVERAGE AIR TEMPERATURE	MIL-L-22851 Ashless Dispersant	COMMERCIAL GRADE
Above 60°F/16°C	SAE 50 or SAE 40	W100 or W80
30°F/-1°C-90°F/32°C	SAE 40	W80
0°F/-18°C-70°F/21°C	SAE 30 or SAE 40	W65 or W80
Below 10°F/-12°C	SAE 30	W65

▶ Fuel Grades

The PA-28 Warrior is certified for use with 100LL fuels.

The table shows the recommended fuel grades. It is wise to pay attention when your aircraft is being refuelled, especially if at an airfield new to you. More than one pilot has found out to their cost that piston engines designed for AVGAS do not run very well on AVTUR (Jet A1). To help guard against this eventuality AVGAS fuelling points carry a RED sticker, and AVTUR fuelling points a BLACK sticker.

The Archer models with the 0-360-A engine may use MOGAS (motor gasoline), ie 4 star petrol, in accordance with detailed procedures and limitations set out by the CAA in an airworthiness notice.

APPROVED FUEL GRADES

100LL

100L

100

Handling the Piper PA-28 Warrior

Handling the Piper PA-28 Warrior

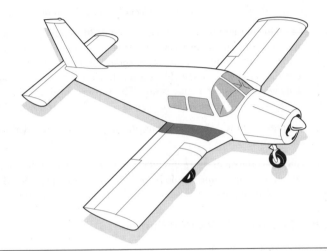

Note: *The information in this section is no substitute for flying instruction under the guidance of a flying instructor familiar with the aircraft and its characteristics.*

▶ Engine Starting

▶ Starting with a Suspected Flooded Engine

▶ Starting in Cold Ambient Conditions (Below 0°C)

▶ Taxying

▶ Power & Pre-take-off Checks

▶ Take-off

▶ Climbing

▶ Cruising Flight

▶ Stalling

▶ Spins

▶ Descent

▶ Landing

▶ Parking and Tie Down

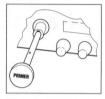

▶Engine Starting

Starting of the Warrior is straightforward, but the ambient conditions and engine temperature are the prime factors to be considered. A cold engine will require between 2 and 4 primes, a hot engine should not require any priming at all. The throttle is set to 1/4" open (that is 1/4 in), with the mixture rich and fuel set to the tank with the lowest contents (unless of course that tank is empty).

Cranking of the starter should be limited to 30 seconds at a time due to the danger of the starter motor overheating. After a prolonged period of engine cranking without a successful start the starter should be allowed a few minutes to cool before a further attempt is made. The starter should not be operated after engine start as damage to the starter may result. The starter warning light should go out after engine start, if it remains lit the engine should be shut down without delay.

"Pumping" of the throttle during starting should be avoided as it can lead to an engine fire on start.

After start the oil pressure should register within 30 seconds. Should the oil pressure not register the engine should be shut down without delay. Readings on the suction gauge and ammeter are also usually checked after engine start.

▶Starting With a Suspected Flooded Engine

An overprimed (flooded) engine will be indicated by weak intermittent firing, and puffs of black smoke from the exhaust during the attempted start. If it is suspected that the engine is flooded (over primed) the throttle should be opened fully and the mixture moved to idle cut off. If the engine starts the throttle should be retarded to the normal position and the mixture moved to fully rich.

▶Starting In Cold Ambient Conditions (below 0°C)

Failure to start due to an underprimed engine is more likely to occur in cold conditions with a cold engine. An underprimed engine will not fire at all, and additional priming is necessary. Starting in cold temperatures will be more difficult due to a number of factors. The oil will be more viscous, the battery may lose up to half of its capacity and the fuel will not vapourise readily. A greater number of primes will be required, external power may be needed to supplement the aircraft battery, and pre-heat may be necessary in very low temperatures.

▶Taxying

In the first few feet of taxying a brake check is normally carried out, followed by steering and differential brake checks in due course. It is common practice to check the hand operated brake lever in addition to the toe brakes (where these are fitted). The direct link, via steering rods, from the rudder pedals to the nose wheel makes the Warrior easy to steer accurately, although on earlier models the steering is quite heavy to operate. Use of differential brake can give a very small turning circle, although increased power is often required when using prolonged differential braking. Where toe brakes are not fitted the brake lever can be used in conjunction with full rudder to reduce turn radius. When taxying with a crosswind

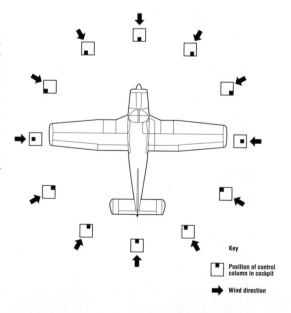

Key

■ Position of control column in cockpit

➡ Wind direction

'opposite rudder' will be required, up to full deflection eg with a crosswind from the left, up to full right rudder may be required as the aircraft tries to 'weathercock' into wind. In this situation differential braking will also aid directional control

The chart shows recommended control column positions when taxying with the prevailing wind from the directions shown.

Speed control is important, especially when taxying over rough surfaces or in strong wind conditions. When slowing the aircraft the throttle should always be closed firstly, and then the brakes evenly applied to slow the aircraft.

During ground operations care should be taken to avoid prolonged idling of the engine, as this may result in fouled spark plugs.

▶ Power And Pre-take-off Checks

The aircraft is usually positioned into wind to aid engine cooling, and before the power checks start the oil temperature should be in the green arc.

The engine is generally run up to 2000 RPM, with the fuel tank with greatest contents selected (the same tank should be used for take-off). At this RPM the carburettor heat is checked, and a small drop in RPM should be noted. The subject of carb icing is covered more fully later, however an important point to note is that the inlet for the 'hot' air is unfiltered, and so dust, grass etc may well enter the engine when 'hot' air is selected, leading to increased engine wear. For this reason the use of carb heat should be kept to the minimum necessary whilst on the ground.

The magnetos are checked individually, with no more than 3 seconds on each magneto being recommended to avoid spark plug fouling. A small drop in RPM is the norm and shows that the ignition system is functioning properly. No RPM drop at all when operating on one magneto may well indicate a malfunction in the ignition system, and the possibility that one or both magnetos are staying 'live'. An excessive drop in RPM when operating on one magneto, especially when accompanied by rough running, may indicate fouled spark plugs or a faulty magneto. If fouled plugs are suspected it may be possible for the pilot to clear the problem. The engine is set to about 2000 RPM with magnetos on 'BOTH', and the mixture leaned to give the 'peak' RPM. This should be held for about 10 seconds, then the mixture is returned to fully rich and the magnetos can be rechecked.

> **WARNING:** Excessive power setting and over lean mixture settings should be avoided during this procedure. If the problem does not clear the aircraft should be considered unfit to fly.

The engine gauges are checked at 2000 RPM for normal indications, together with the suction gauge and ammeter.

▶Take-off

Normally take-off is made with the mixture in the fully RICH position. At high elevation airfields (above say 3000' AMSL) it may be necessary to lean the mixture before take-off to give max power.

For all take-offs care must be taken to ensure that the feet remain clear of the toe brakes (where these are fitted), this is best done by keeping your heels on the floor. It should also be positively confirmed that the brake lever is fully OFF.

At the start of the take-off run (as at all other times), the throttle should be opened smoothly and progressively – rapid opening of the throttle should be specifically avoided. The normal rotate speed is 50kts, with a climb speed of 80 knots dependent on conditions and operator procedures. In crosswind conditions the rotate speed should be increased to ensure full control immediately after take-off. For 'short field' take-offs the use of 2 stages of flap (25°) is common practice, with a slower climb out speed.

On rough surfaces particularly, it is important to protect the nose wheel by keeping weight off it during the take-off run, although 'over-rotating' should be avoided as this will lengthen the take-off run (and ruin the view ahead!).

▶Climbing

An airspeed in the region of 79 Knots will give the best rate of climb after take-off. The best angle of climb (the best increase in height for the shortest distance travelled over the ground), can be obtained at about 63 knots. During climbing it is important to monitor the engine gauges, as the engine is operating at a high power setting but with a reduced cooling airflow compared to cruising flight. Lookout ahead is impaired by the high nose attitude, and it is common practice to 'weave' the nose periodically during the climb to visually check the area ahead.

▶Cruising Flight

Engine Handling:

Engine rough running can be caused by a number of factors. It should be remembered that the majority of engine failures in light aircraft are caused by pilot error. After carburettor icing, fuel exhaustion (running out of fuel) or fuel starvation (ie fuel on-board but not reaching the engine) are common causes of engine failure. Having sufficient fuel on board to complete the flight is a point of basic airmanship, and mostly accomplished through proper flight planning and thorough pre-flight checks. Keeping the fuel tanks in balance and monitoring the fuel system is a part of the cruise checks. When the fuel tanks are changed in flight the electric fuel pump should be turned On before the change, and left on until about 30 seconds after the change. Fuel starvation may occur if the engine driven fuel pump fails, in this instance the use of the electric fuel pump should restore the fuel supply to the engine and allow for a diversion to be made.

Regular monitoring of the engine instruments may forewarn of an impending problem. HIGH OIL TEMPERATURE may indicate a faulty gauge, if not accompanied by a corresponding drop in oil pressure. As with most instances the action to be taken will depend on the pilot's judgment of the situation at the time. As general guidance a diversion to a suitable airfield, whilst remaining alert to the possibility of a sudden engine failure would make a reasonable course of action. **Where high oil temperature is accompanied by a low oil pressure, engine failure may very well be imminent, and the pilot should act accordingly.** That said such a situation might occur during a prolonged slow climb in hot conditions, in this instance increasing the airspeed to provide more cooling, and reducing power if possible, may restore oil temperature to normal. In the event of a LOW OIL PRESSURE reading, accompanied by a normal oil temperature reading, gauge failure may be the culprit, and the pilot can consider actions similar to those for an oil temperature gauge failure.

▶Stalling

A Reminder: The information in this section is no substitute for flying instruction under the guidance of a flying instructor familiar with the aircraft and its characteristics.

The aircraft is generally straightforward in its stalling behaviour. The stall warning horn activates 5 to 10 knots above the stall airspeed. Because it is electrically operated, it is inoperative with the master switch off, or with a faulty electrical system. The actual stall speed can be affected by many factors including the aircraft weight and centre of gravity position. The use of power will lower the stalling speed, whilst turning flight raises the stall speed. The use of flaps, power or turning flight considerably increases the chances of a wing drop at the stall, when practising stalls the possibility of a wing drop can be reduced by keeping the aircraft in balance during the approach to the stall. Typical height loss for a full stall with a conventional recovery (using power) is about 200'. A gentle stall and absence of wing drop characterise the Warrior stall, the stall is preceded by mild airframe buffeting and gentle pitching.

In-service experience has shown that the aircraft may roll sharply to the right whilst stalling with high power settings and aft CG positions. To cure this problem a temporary aft CG position restriction was introduced, while leading edge stall strips were fitted to the wing. Check the status of the aircraft if planning to practice stalling.

▶Spins

The Warrior, Cadet and Archer ARE NOT CLEARED for intentional spinning. Should an inadvertent spin occur the recommended spin recovery is:

- ■ Check ailerons neutral and throttle closed
- ■ Apply and maintain full opposite rudder (opposite to the direction of spin)
- ■ Move the control wheel fully forward.
- ■ When rotation stops centralise the rudder and recover from the ensuing dive.

▶Descent

The descent may be powered or glide, for the glide a speed of about 70 knots is standard. Where flaps are used the rate of descent increases, the initial lowering of flap leads to a definite nose-up pitching and reduced airspeed. The low power settings usually used during the descent, and a possible prolonged descent into warmer air, provide ideal conditions for carburettor icing, full carburettor heat should be used where necessary. In a glide descent power should be added for short periods throughout the descent to help prevent plug fouling, rapid cylinder cooling and of course carb. icing.

▶ Landing

For the approach to landing the mixture should be fully RICH (unless landing at a very high elevation airfield), the electric fuel pump should be on and the fuel tank with the greatest contents selected. The aircraft is not difficult to land, however in common with most light aircraft care should be taken to protect the nosewheel.

As already covered the nosewheel is nowhere near as strong as the main undercarriage, but there is no need for its strength to be tested if a proper approach and landing technique is used. Approach speed for a normal approach with flap is about 70 knots, usually a little higher for a flapless approach. Incorrect approach speed is a primary cause of 'ballooning', which often leads to bouncing. Bouncing also arises where the aircraft is allowed to touch down at too high a speed, usually in a level attitude rather than a nose up attitude. The correct action in either a 'balloon' or a bounce is to GO AROUND without delay. The correct landing technique is to approach at the proper speed, 'flare' or 'hold off' for landing, close the throttle, and gradually raise the nose to ensure a slow touch down speed on the MAINWHEELS FIRST, with the nose wheel still off the ground. As the aircraft slows down correct use of the stabilator means the nose wheel is allowed to gently contact the surface some time after the initial mainwheel contact. Again there is no substitute for flying instruction in the proper technique with a flying instructor.

The go-around does not pose any particular problems, even with full flap extended. The trim change when applying full power is manageable, and although the aircraft will climb with full flap extended, it is common practice to raise flaps to the 2nd stage (25°) as part of the immediate go-around actions. During the go-around, as at all other times, the throttle should be opened smoothly, from idle to full throttle is not less than 2 seconds. This is done specifically to avoid the accelerator pump causing an over rich mixture and consequent loss of power.

▶Parking and Tie Down

The aircraft is generally parked into wind, it is good practice to stop with the nosewheel straight so that the rudder is not deflected. All switches should be off, and the doors closed. In extremely cold weather it may advisable NOT to set the parking brake as moisture may freeze the brakes, in addition the parking brake should not be set if there is reason to believe that the brakes are overheated. If for any reason the parking brake is not set the wheels should be 'chocked'.

When tying down the aircraft the following technique is recommended:

- Park aircraft into wind with the flaps retracted.
- Secure the flying controls by looping the seat belt through the control wheel.
- Tie ropes, cables or chains to the wing tie down points and secure to ground anchor points with the ropes etc at approx 45° to the ground.
- If desired a rope (not cable or chain) can be secured to the nose leg and secured to a ground anchor point.
- A rope can be passed through the tail tie down point and each end secured at 45° angle to the ground each side of the tail.
- External control locks may be advisable in strong or gusty wind conditions.

It is also prudent to use a pitot cover, particularly if the aircraft will be left unattended for some time.

Mixture and Carb Icing Supplement

Mixture and Carb Icing Supplement

▶ Carburettor Icing

▶ How Carburettor Icing Forms

▶ Conditions Likely to Lead to Carburettor Icing

▶ Carburettor Icing Conditions

▶ Symptoms of Carburettor Icing

▶ Use of Carburettor Heat

▶ Mixture Control

▶ Reasons for Adjusting the Mixture

▶ Effect of Mixture Adjustment

▶ Use of the Mixture Control

▶Carburettor Icing

Almost certainly the most common cause of engine rough running, and complete engine failures, is carburettor icing. Despite this carburettor icing remains a widely misunderstood subject, with many pilots' knowledge of the subject being limited to a feeling that the carb heat should be used regularly in flight, without really knowing the symptoms of carb. icing or the conditions most likely to cause its formation.

▶How Carburettor Icing Forms

IMPACT ICING occurs when ice forms over the external air inlet (air filter) and inside the induction system leading to the carburettor. This type of icing occurs with the temperature below 0°C whilst flying in cloud, or in precipitation (ie rain, sleet or snow). These conditions are also conducive to airframe icing, and this aircraft is NOT CLEARED FOR FLIGHT INTO KNOWN ICING CONDITIONS, which clearly these are. So, assuming the aircraft is operated legally within its limitations, this form of icing should not occur, and is not considered further.

CARBURETTOR ICING is caused by a temperature drop inside the carburettor, which can happen even in conditions where other forms of icing will not occur. The causes of this temperature drop are twofold:

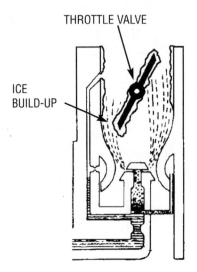

THROTTLE VALVE

ICE
BUILD-UP

1 FUEL ICING – the evaporation of fuel inside the carburettor. Liquid fuel changes to fuel vapour and mixes with the induction air causing a large temperature drop. If the temperature inside the carburettor falls below 0°C, water vapour in the atmosphere condenses into ice, usually on the walls of the carburettor passage adjacent to the fuel jet, and on the throttle valve. Generally fuel icing is responsible for around 70% of the temperature drop in the carburettor.

2 THROTTLE ICING – the temperature loss caused by the acceleration of air and consequent pressure drop around the throttle valve. This effect may again take the temperature below 0°C, and water vapour in the inlet air will condense into ice on the throttle valve. This practical effect is a demonstration of Bernoulli's Principle.

As fuel and throttle icing generally occur together, they are considered just as carburettor icing.

▶Conditions Likely To Lead To Carburettor Icing

Two criteria govern the likelihood of carburettor icing conditions, the AIR TEMPERATURE and the RELATIVE HUMIDITY.

The ambient air temperature is important, BUT NOT BECAUSE THE TEMPERATURE NEEDS TO BE BELOW 0°C, OR EVEN CLOSE TO FREEZING. The temperature drop in the carburettor can be up to 30°C, so carburettor icing can (and does) occur in hot ambient conditions. No wonder carburettor icing is sometimes referred to as refrigeration icing. Carburettor icing is considered a possibility within the temperature range of -10°C to +30°C.

The relative humidity (a measure of the water content of the atmosphere) is the major factor. The greater the water content in the atmosphere (the higher the relative humidity), the greater the risk of carburettor icing. That said the relative humidity (RH) does not to have to be 100% (ie visible water droplets – cloud, rain), for carburettor icing to occur. Carburettor icing is considered a possibility at relative humidity values as low as 30%, but it is rare that the RH gets this low in Europe. Herein lies the real danger of carburettor icing, that it can occur in such a wide range of conditions. Obviously the pilot must be alert to the possibility of carburettor icing at just about all times. Flight in or near cloud, or in other visible moisture (ie rain) might be an obvious cause of carburettor icing, but – VISIBLE MOISTURE DOES NOT NEED TO BE PRESENT FOR CARBURETTOR ICING TO OCCUR.

Carburettor Icing Conditions

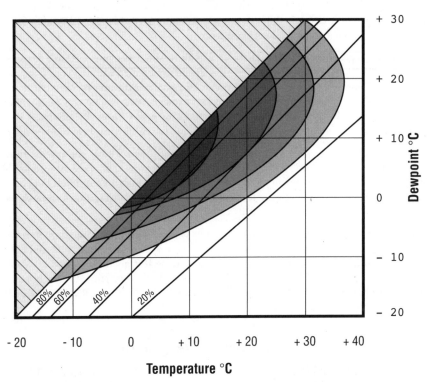

 100% Relative humidity

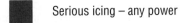 Serious icing – any power

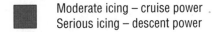 Moderate icing – cruise power
Serious icing – descent power

 Serious icing – descent power

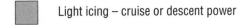 Light icing – cruise or descent power

▶ Symptoms Of Carburettor Icing

In this aircraft, fitted with a fixed pitch propeller, the symptoms of carburettor icing are straightforward. A loss of RPM will be the first symptom, although this is often first noticed as a loss of altitude. As the icing becomes more serious, engine rough running may occur.

Carburettor icing is often detected during the use of the carburettor heat. Normally when the carburettor heat is used, a small drop in rpm occurs, when the control is returned to cold (off) the rpm restores to the same as before the use of carburettor heat. If the rpm restores to a higher figure than before the carburettor heat was used, it can be reasonably supposed that some form of carburettor icing was present.

▶ Use Of Carburettor Heat

Apart from the normal check of carburettor heat during the power checks, it may be necessary to use the carburettor heat on the ground if carburettor icing is suspected. Safety considerations apart, the use of carburettor heat on the ground should be kept to a minimum, as the hot air inlet is unfiltered, and so sand or dust can enter the engine, increasing engine wear.

Carburettor icing is generally considered to be very unlikely with the engine operating at above 75% power, ie during the take-off and climb. Carburettor heat should not be used with the engine operating at above 75% power (ie full throttle) as detonation may occur. Detonation is the uncontrolled burning of fuel in the cylinders, literally an explosion, and will cause serious damage to the engine very quickly. Apart from the danger of detonation, the use of carburettor heat reduces the power the engine produces. In any situation where full power is required (ie take-off, climb, go-around) the carburettor heat must be off (cold).

Very few operators recommend the use of anything other than FULL carburettor heat. A normal carburettor icing check will involve leaving the carburettor heat on (hot) for 5-10 seconds, although the pilot may wish to vary this dependent on the conditions. The use of carburettor heat does increase the fuel consumption, and this may be a factor to consider if the aircraft is being flown towards the limit of its range/endurance in possible carburettor icing conditions.

With carburettor icing present, the use of carburettor heat may lead to a large drop in rpm, with rough running. The instinctive reaction is to put the carburettor heat back to cold (off), and quickly. This is, however, the wrong action. Chances are this rough running is a good thing, and the carburettor heat should be left on (hot) until the rough running clears and the rpm rises. In this instance the use of carburettor heat has melted a large amount of accumulated icing and the melted ice is passing through the engine, causing temporary rough running.

Carburettor heat control

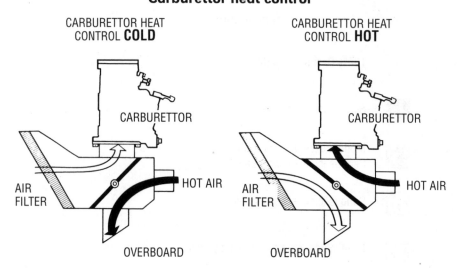

CARBURETTOR HEAT
CONTROL **COLD**

CARBURETTOR

AIR
FILTER

HOT AIR

OVERBOARD

CARBURETTOR HEAT
CONTROL **HOT**

CARBURETTOR

AIR
FILTER

HOT AIR

OVERBOARD

Care should be taken when flying in very cold ambient conditions (below -10°C). In these conditions the use of carburettor heat may actually raise the temperature in the carburettor to that most conducive to carburettor icing. Generally when the temperature in the carburettor is below -8°C moisture forms directly into ice crystals which pass through the engine.

The rpm loss normally associated with the use of carburettor heat is caused by the reduced density of the hot air entering the carburettor, leading to an over rich mixture entering the engine. If the carburettor heat has to be left constantly on (hot) – ie flight in heavy rain and cloud – it may be advisable to lean the mixture in order to maintain rpm and smooth engine running.

It is during the descent (and particularly the glide descent) that carburettor icing is most likely to occur. The position of the throttle valve (ie almost closed) is a contributory factor, and even though the carburettor heat is normally applied throughout a glide descent, the low engine power will reduce the temperature of the hot air selected with the carburettor heat control. In addition a loss of power may not be readily noticed. The propeller is likely to windmill even after a complete loss of power and so a full loss of power may only be apparent when the throttle is opened at the bottom of the descent. This is one good reason for opening the throttle to 'warm the engine' at intervals during a glide descent.

▶The Mixture Control

The aircraft is provided with a mixture control so that the pilot can adjust the fuel/air mixture entering the engine when necessary. The cockpit mixture control operates a needle valve between the float bowl and the main metering jet. This valve controls the fuel flow to the main metering jet to adjust the mixture, with the mixture control in the ICO position (fully lean) the valve is fully closed.

▶Reasons For Adjusting The Mixture

Correct leaning of the engine will enable the engine to be operated at its most efficient in terms of fuel consumption. With the increased use of 100LL fuel, leaning is also important to reduce spark plug fouling.

The most efficient engine operation is obtained with a fuel/air ratio of about 1:15, that is 1 part fuel to 15 parts air. In fact with the mixture set to fully rich, the system is designed to give a slightly richer mixture than ideal, typically about 1:12. This slightly over rich mixture reduces the possibility of pre-ignition or detonation, and aids cylinder cooling.

As altitude increases the air density decreases. Above about 3000' the reduced air density can lead to an over rich mixture. If the mixture becomes excessively rich, power will be lost, rough running may be evident and ultimately engine failure will occur due to a 'rich cut'. It is for this reason that the mixture control is provided to ensure the correct fuel/air ratio, typically it is used when cruising above 3000'.

The flight manuals for some older aircraft recommend leaning only above 5000'. However with the increasing use of AVGAS 100LL, and the plug fouling problems sometimes associated with 100LL, most operators recommend leaning once above 3000'.

Effect of Mixture Adjustment

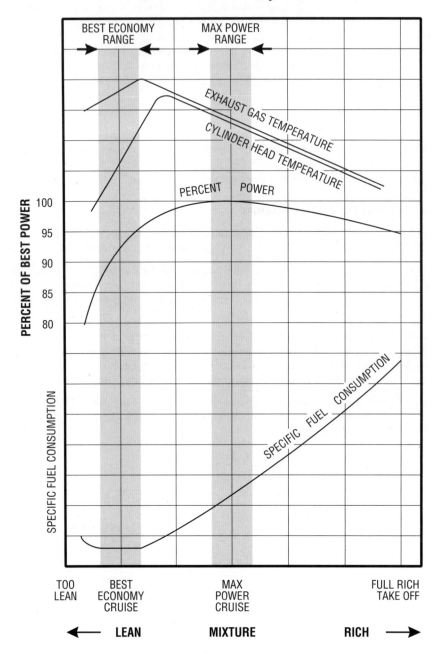

▶Use Of The Mixture Control

For take-off and climb the mixture should be fully rich, the only exception being operation from a high density altitude airport when leaning may be necessary to ensure the availability of max. power. On reaching a cruising altitude above about 3000' the cruise power should be set, and then leaning can be carried out (note: generally leaning with over 75% power set is not recommended). If climbing above about 5000', full throttle will be less than 75% power on a normally aspirated engine and so leaning may be permissible to maintain smooth running.

Assuming that there is no Exhaust Gas Temperature (EGT) gauge and no cylinder head temperature gauge, the primary instrument to watch when leaning is the RPM gauge (tachometer).

To lean the engine, the recommended power setting (RPM) is set with the throttle. Next, with a constant throttle setting, the mixture control is slowly moved back (leaned). If leaning is required the RPM will increase slowly, peak, and then decrease as the mixture is leaned, if leaning is continued the engine will ultimately run rough and lose power.

If the mixture is set to achieve peak RPM, the maximum power mixture has been achieved.

If the mixture is set to give a tachometer reading 25-50RPM less than peak rpm on the 'lean' side, the best economy mixture has been achieved. This setting is the one that many aircraft manufacturers recommend (25-50 RPM on the 'lean side' of peak RPM), and their performance claims are based on such a procedure.

Using a mixture that is too lean is a false economy, and will lead to serious engine damage sooner or later. Detonation (an uncontrolled explosive combustion of the mixture in the cylinder) is particularly dangerous, and can lead to an engine failure in a very short time. The use of a fully rich mixture during full power operations is specifically to ensure engine cooling and guard against detonation.

For any change in operating conditions (altitude, power setting) the mixture will need to be reset. It is particularly important that the mixture is set to fully rich before increasing the power setting.

During a descent from a high altitude, the mixture will gradually become too lean if not reset, leading to excessive cylinder temperatures, power loss and ultimately engine failure. Normally the mixture is set to fully rich prior to landing, unless operating at a high elevation airfield.

Moving the mixture to the fully lean position – ICO (Idle Cut Off) – closes the needle valve and so stops fuel supply to the main metering jet. This is the normal method for closing down the engine and ensures that no unburnt mixture is left in the engine.

NORMAL COMBUSTION   DETONATION

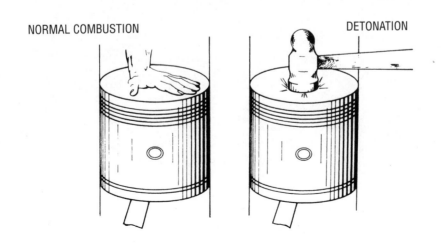

Expanded
Piper PA-28 Warrior
Pre-flight Checklist

Expanded Piper PA-28 Warrior Pre-flight Checklist

▶ Approaching Aircraft

▶ In Cabin

▶ Starboard Wing

▶ Starboard Undercarriage

▶ Front Fuselage and Engine

▶ Port Undercarriage

▶ Port Wing

▶ Port Fuselage

▶ Starboard Fuselage

▶Approaching Aircraft

Check for and remove any tie downs, external control locks, pitot cover and wheel chocks.

Look for any oil & fuel spillages from aircraft.

Remove any ice & frost from ALL surfaces.

Check for access to taxiways, obstructions, loose gravel etc.

Look to see if aircraft is on a level surface. A sloping surface will affect the visual check of fuel contents.

▶In Cabin

1 **Internal Control locks & Covers** ....Remove & Stow Securely

2 **Parking Brake** ....Check On with locking plate in

3 **Magneto Switches** ....Check OFF and Key Out

4 **Master Switch** ....On
     Turn on Pitot heater,anti-collision beacon, landing light and
     navigation lights.
     Leave cockpit and check in turn:

5 **Stall Warner Vane** ....Move gently forward to check

6 **Pitot Heat** ....Check with fingers that pressure head is warm
     (it may take a minute or so to warm up)

7 **Anti-Collision Beacon**.................Check operation (rotating red light on tail)

8 **Landing/Nav lights**......................Check
     For Navigation lights colours are:
     PORT(Left) – RED;
     STARBOARD (Right) – GREEN;
     REAR (Tail) – WHITE

Return to cockpit and turn off electrical services as in above

9 **Fuel** ....Turn On
     Check contents gauges

10 **Master Switch** ....Off

11 **Flaps** ....Lower to 2nd Stage (25°)

12 **Trimmer**.......................................Check position neutral using indicator

13 **First Aid Kit**..................................In Position,secure

14 **Fire Extinguisher**.........................In Position,secure & serviceable
     (gauge at top should be in green arc)

15 **On leaving cockpit do NOT tread on flap surface**

External

Begin at rear of wing. This should also be where you complete your checks.

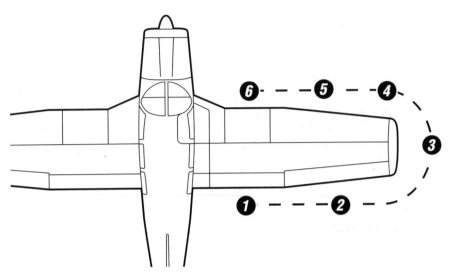

▶ Starboard Wing

1 **Flap**...Upper and lower surface condition. Particularly check inner lower surface for caked mud or stone damage from wheels.
Check linkages secure and greased

2 **Aileron**...Upper and lower surface condition, linkages & hinges secure, balance weight (inside wing tip) secure (with fingers inside hinge line hold the aileron with other hand – sudden down movement of aileron makes efficient cutting action!)
Check full and free movement – DO NOT USE FORCE

3 **Wing Tip**.......................................Condition, Security. Navigation light unbroken.
(This area is particularly vulnerable to hanger damage)

4 **Wing Surface**...............................Upper & Lower surface condition

5 **Wing Leading Edge**....................Check for dents along entire length

6 **Fuel Tank**.....................................Check contents visually, resecure cap.
Check fuel vent unblocked. Take fuel drain sample from under tank if necessary – check for correct colour, water bubbles or sediment.
Check drain not leaking

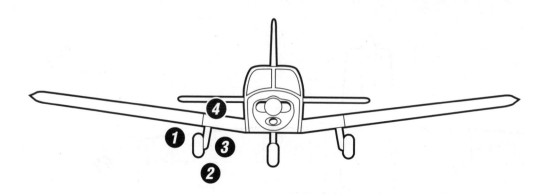

▶ Starboard Undercarriage

1 **Tyre**...Check for tread & general condition.
                                                      Check for correct inflation. Look for alignment of creep marks

2 **Hydraulic Lines**...........................Check for leaks (red fluid)

3 **Disc Brake**....................................Should be shiny, not rusty or pitted

4 **Oleo**..Check extension. Look for mud or stone damage on wing & flap
                                                      surface near undercarriage

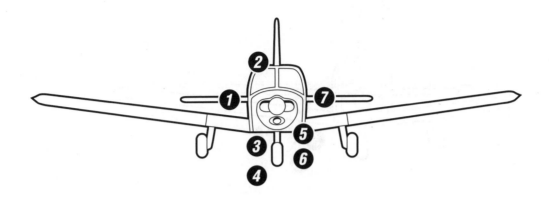

▶Front Fuselage & Engine

1 **Starboard Cowling**......................Open engine compartment, check oil level, do NOT overtighten dipstick on resecuring.
Check engine compartment generally
(ie HT leads secure,oil leaks) Resecure cowling

2 **Windscreen**..................................Should be clean and insect free, OAT probe secure

3 **Nose Leg** ....Oleo extension, linkages, nuts & split pins secure

4 **Nose Wheel**..................................Check for tread & general condition.
Check for correct inflation.
Check alignment of creep marks

5 **Front Cowling**..............................Check condition & security. Intakes clear, Landing light unbroken

6 **Propeller**.......................................Look for cracks or chips especially leading edge.
Check spinner secure and condition good.
DO NOT MOVE OR SWING PROPELLER

7 **Port Cowling** ....Open cowling and check brake fluid level
Check engine compartment (ie HT leads secure etc). Resecure cowling. Take fuel sample if necc.
Check fuel drain not leaking

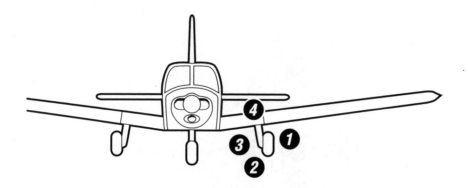

▶Port Undercarriage

1   Tyre ....Check for tread & general condition.
                                     Check for correct inflation.
                                     Check alignment of creep marks

2   Hydraulic Lines.............................Check for leaks (red fluid)

3   Disc Brake ....Should be shiny, not rusty or pitted

4   Oleo..Check for correct extension. Look for mud or stone damage on
                                     wing & flap surface near undercarriage

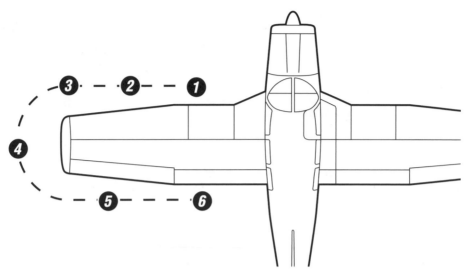

▶Port Wing

1 **Fuel Tank** ....Check contents visually, resecure cap.
Take fuel drain sample if necessary.
Check drain not leaking

2 **Wing Leading Edge** ....Check for dents along entire length.
Check pressure head
DO NOT BLOW INTO PERFORATIONS

3 **Wing Surface** ....Upper & Lower surface condition

4 **Wing Tip** ....Condition,Security. Navigation light unbroken

5 **Aileron** ....Upper and lower surface condition,linkages & hinges secure,
balance weight (inside wing tip) secure. Remember to watch for
aileron movement whilst checking inside hinge line.
Check full and free movement gently
DO NOT USE FORCE

6 **Flap** ....Upper and lower surface condition esp. near undercarriage.
Check linkages secure and greased

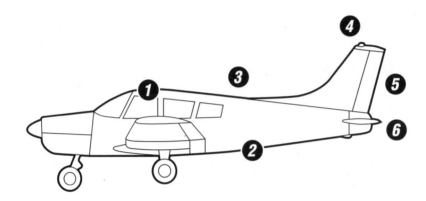

▶ Port Fuselage

1 **Windows** ....Clean & uncracked

2 **Skin**..General surface condition upper and lower, look for wrinkles, dents or punctures

3 **Radio Aerials** ....Check secure

4 **Tail Fin**..Check skin condition,especially fairings; Check aerials and rotating beacon secure

5 **Rudder** ....Check condition, linkages secure & greased, nuts & split pins secure, Nav light unbroken.
DO NOT ATTEMPT TO FORCE RUDDER MOVEMENT

6 **Stabilator**....................................Check upper and lower surface condition.
Check linkages and split pins.
Check full and free movement DO NOT USE FORCE.
Ensure anti-balance tab moves in correct sense.
Check other side of tail fin

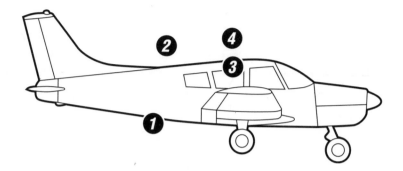

▶Starboard Fuselage

1 **Skin**..General surface condition, upper and lower, look for any
wrinkles, dents or punctures

2 **Radio Aerials** ....Check secure. Do not tread on flap surface

3 **Cockpit door** ....Check latches & hinges secure

4 **Windows** ....Check clean & uncracked

---

IMPORTANT

REMEMBER: FULL REFERENCE MUST BE MADE TO AIRCRAFT FLIGHT MANUAL, PILOTS OPERATING HANDBOOK, AIPs, FLYING SCHOOL SYLLABUS/PILOTS ORDER BOOK, ETC

IF IN DOUBT – ASK

Loading and
Performance

Loading and Performance

▶ Loading

▶ Mathematical Weight and Balance Calculation

▶ Use of the Loading Graph

▶ Performance

▶ PA-28 Warrior Take-off and Landing Performance Graphs

▶ Take-off Performance

▶ Take-off Distance Calculation Example

▶ Landing Performance

▶ Landing Distance Calculation Example

▶ Enroute Performance

▶ Runway Dimensions

▶ Loading

Aircraft loading can divided into two areas, the aircraft weight and the centre of gravity (c.g) position.

The aircraft must be loaded so that its weight is below the certified maximum take-off weight (2440lbs/1106Kg for the Warrior II) or (2550lbs/1156kg for the Archer II). The flight manual may also list a 'ramp weight', which is the maximum permissible weight for taxying prior to take-off. The difference between this and the maximum take-off weight allows for the fuel used in taxying and power checks. The weight limit is set primarily as a function of the lifting capability of the aircraft, which is largely determined by the wing design and engine power of the aircraft. Operating the aircraft when it is over weight will adversely effect the aircraft handling and performance, such as:

> Increased take-off speed and slower acceleration
>
> Increased runway length required for take-off
>
> Reduced rate of climb
>
> Reduced maximum altitude capability
>
> Reduced range and endurance
>
> Reduction in manoeuvrability and controllability
>
> Increased stall speed
>
> Increased approach and landing speed
>
> Increased runway length required for landing

The aircraft must also be loaded to ensure that its centre of gravity (c.g.) is within set limits, normally defined as a forward and aft limit in inches aft of the datum. The forward limit is determined by the amount of elevator control available at landing speed, the aft limit is determined by the stability and controllability of the aircraft whilst manoeuvering. Attempted flight with the c.g. position outside of the set limits (either forward or aft) will lead to control difficulties, and quite possibly loss of control of the aircraft.

When loading the aircraft it is standard practice to calculate the weight and c.g. position of the aircraft at the same time, commonly known as the weight and balance calculation. Before going further it must be emphasised that the following examples are provided for illustrative purposes only. Each INDIVIDUAL aircraft has an INDIVIDUAL weight schedule that is valid only for that aircraft, and is dependent amongst other things on the equipment fitted to the aircraft. If the aircraft has any major modification, repair or new equipment fitted a new weight schedule will be produced. Therefore in any loading or performance calculations you must use the documents for the specific aircraft you will be using. As well as setting out limits the aircraft documents will also give lever arms for each item of loading. The lever arm is a distance from the aircraft datum to the item. The weight multiplied by its lever arm gives its moment. Thus a set weight will have a greater moment the further away it is from the datum.

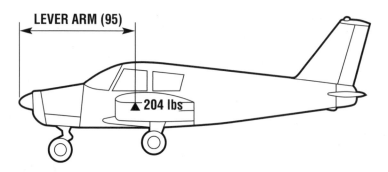

LEVER ARM (95) x WEIGHT (204) = MOMENT (19380)

The operating weight of the aircraft can be split into three categories:

STANDARD (EMPTY) WEIGHT – the weight of the aircraft, including unuseable fuel (and normally full oil). The weight and c.g. position of the aircraft in this condition will be noted in the weight schedule.

VARIABLE LOAD – weight of the crew (ie pilot). The certified minimum crew for this aircraft is one pilot (!). The weight schedule will give the lever arm for this load.

DISPOSABLE LOAD – weight of passengers, fuel and baggage. Again the weight schedule will give a lever arm for each of these loads.

Firstly the pilot will need to calculate a weight for the variable and disposable load. It is obviously important to work in one set of units (either lbs or kgs). This becomes more complicated for the fuel load where volume (litres, imperial gallons or U S gallons) will need to be converted into weight. This may be done in the weight schedule, but conversion tables are set out in section 7.

Weight And Centre Of Gravity Schedule

PRODUCED BY :

GROSVENOR AVIATION SERVICES (ENGINEERING) LIMITED

AIRCRAFT TYPE: **PIPER PA38-112**

NATIONALITY AND
REGISTRATION MARKS: **G-BGRR**

CONSTRUCTOR'S SERIAL No: **78A0336**

MAXIMUM PERMISSIBLE WEIGHT: **1670lbs**

MAXIMUM LANDING WEIGHT: **1670lbs**

CENTRE OF GRAVITY LIMITS: **REFER TO FLIGHT MANUAL REP No. FAA 2126**

ALL LEVER ARMS ARE DISTANCES IN INCHES EITHER FORE OR AFT OF DATUM.

PART 'A' BASIC WEIGHT

The basic weight of this aircraft as calculated from Planeweighs Limited

Report No.1034 weighed on 08.07.88. at Manchester Airport is: **1182lbs**

The centre of gravity of aircraft in the same condition (aft of the datum) is: **74.66 ins**.

The total Moment about the datum in this condition in lb ins. is: **88254.45**

The DATUM referred to is defined in the Flight Manual, which is **66.25 ins**. forward of Wing leading edge.

The basic weight includes the weight of 12lbs unuseable fuel and 45lbs of oil and the weight of items indicated in Appendix 1 which comprises the list of basic equipment carried.

Each individual aircraft has an individual weight schedule, valid only for that aircraft. The weight schedule will state lever arms for each item of loading

▶Mathematical Weight And Balance Calculation

With this method of calculation the weights of each item are listed together with their lever arm. Addition of all the weights is the first step, to ensure that the resulting figure is within the maximum permitted. Assuming this is the case the balance can then be calculated. For each item (except for the basic weight where the calculation is done already on the weight schedule) the weight is multiplied by the lever arm, to give a moment. Normally the lever arm is aft of the datum, to give a positive figure. If the lever arm quoted is forward of the datum the moment will be negative (although obviously the weight is NOT deducted from the weight calculation). All the moments are then added together, to give the total moment, and this figure is then divided by the total weight. The resulting figure will be the position of the c.g. , which can be checked to ensure it is within the set limits. The weight and c.g. position can be plotted on a graph in the flight manual. If the plotted position is within the 'envelope', the weight and c.g. position are within limits.

It is obviously important for the pilot to be sure of whether the aircraft needs to operated in the NORMAL or UTILITY categories. The aircraft flight manual will advise which manoeuvres can only be carried out when the aircraft is in the utility category. Operation in the utility category is defined as a reduced weight (2070lbs/939Kg for the Warrior II), (2130lbs/966kg for the Archer II) and different c.g. limits. Also baggage in the rear baggage area and rear seat passengers are not permitted. The critical importance of the fuel load in the calculation of c.g. position for utility category operations should be remembered.

Example:

BASIC(EMPTY) WEIGHT: Aircraft G-AAAA
                                  From the weight schedule for this aircraft,
                                  weight is 1514.90lbs

VARIABLE LOAD: Pilot 160lbs

DISPOSABLE LOAD: Co-Pilot 140lbs
                                  Fuel (level with tabs) 34 US gal @ 6.0lbs per
                                  US gal = 204lbs

Although at this stage you can simply add together the weights to check the all up weight, it is more common to make up a table to check weight AND balance. Using the information above, and the lever arms from the weight schedule, we can make up a table to calculate the moment for each item (remembering that weight x lever arm gives the moment).

ITEM	WEIGHT	LEVER ARM	MOMENT
BASIC (EMPTY) WEIGHT – from the weight schedule for G-AAAA the weight, lever arm and moment are all listed			
G-AAAA	1514.9	87.13	131988.13
VARIABLE LOAD			
Pilot	160.0	80.5	12880.00
DISPOSABLE LOAD			
Passenger	140	80.5	11270.00
Fuel	204	95.0	19380.00
TOTAL WEIGHT	2018.9	TOTAL MOMENT	175518.13

The total weight is below the maximum permitted, and so is acceptable.

Dividing the total moment by the total weight gives the Centre of Gravity position:

$$\frac{175518.13}{2018.9} = 86.94 \text{ inches aft of datum}$$

When this weight and CG position is plotted on the relevant graph in the flight manual, it can be seen that the aircraft is loaded to be within the UTILITY category.

PA 28 WARRIOR WEIGHT VS C.G. ENVELOPE

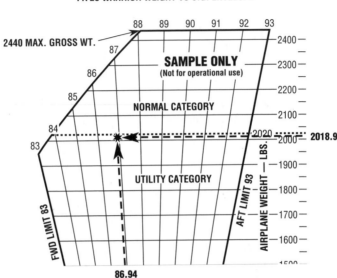

Out of interest it is worth doing this exercise again, but now assuming full fuel, some rear passengers and a little baggage:

ITEM	WEIGHT	LEVER ARM	MOMENT
BASIC (EMPTY) WEIGHT – the weight, lever arm and moment are listed in the weight schedule			
for G-AAAA)	1514.9	87.13	131988.13
VARIABLE LOAD			
Pilot	160.0	80.5	12880.0
DISPOSABLE LOAD			
Passenger	140	80.5	11270.0
Fuel	288	95.0	27360.0
2x Rear seat Pax	300	118.1	35430.0
rear baggage	20	142.8	2856.0
TOTAL WEIGHT	2422.9	TOTAL MOMENT	221784.13

The total weight is below the maximum permitted, although now we are out of the utility category and into the normal category.

Dividing the total moment by the total weight gives the Centre of Gravity position:

$$\frac{221784.13}{2422.9} = 91.54 \text{ inches aft of datum}$$

When the weight and CG position is plotted on the graph in the flight manual, it can be seen that the aircraft is loaded to be within the NORMAL category. However you can see that we are only allowing for some fairly light people and virtually no baggage. As Piper themselves point out you are unlikely to be able to fill a Warrior with four adults, full fuel and full baggage and still be within limits. It is down to the pilot in command to decide what to leave on the ground!

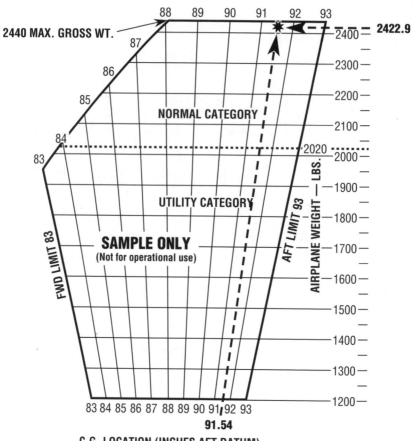

C.G. LOCATION (INCHES AFT DATUM)

▶ Use Of The Loading Graph

The problem with the mathematical methods is the time and amount of maths involved. Here the loading graph can help by multiplying the load by the lever arm for you. Using the figures from the second loading example before, the loading graph will look like this:

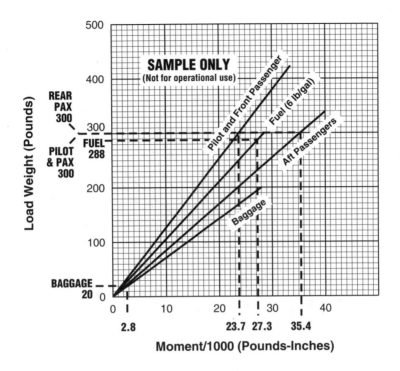

These figures can now go into a simplified table:

ITEM	WEIGHT	MOMENT/1000
G-AAAA	1514.9	132
Pilot & Passenger	300	23.7
Fuel	288	27.3
Rear Passenger	300	35.4
Rear Baggage	20	2.8
Total Weight = 2422.9		Total Moment/1000 = 221.2

Again total moment (/1000) is divided by total weight (/1000)

$$\frac{221.2}{2.4229} = 91.29 \text{ inches aft of datum}$$

The slightly different result is due to the less exact nature of using the loading graph. If in any doubt, or if the result is close to the edge of the CG envelope, the mathematical method should be used.

A WORD OF WARNING. As well as the safety aspect, operating the aircraft outside its weight and balance envelope has far reaching legal and financial implications. Almost the first thing an accident investigator will check after an accident is the loading of the aircraft. If the loading is outside limits the pilot is contravening the Air Navigation Order. In addition both the aircraft insurance company and your personal insurance company will be unsympathetic when they know that the conditions of the Certificate of Airworthiness (ie the flight manual limitations) were not complied with. As the pilot in command the responsibility is yours alone. The fact that the aircraft has four seats does not necessarily mean that the aircraft can be flown with all four seats occupied, baggage and full fuel load.

PA 28 Warrior Loading Graph

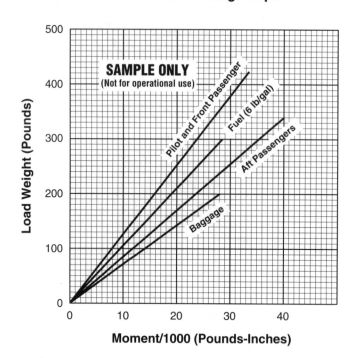

PA 28 Warrior Weight and Centre of Gravity Envelope

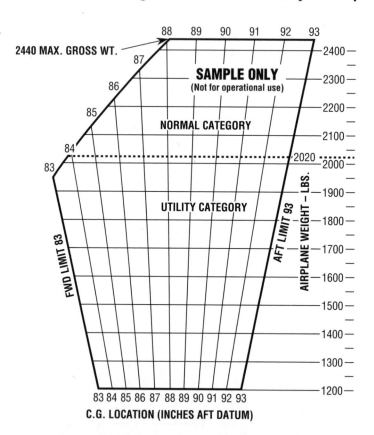

▶ Performance

The aircraft flight manual contains a section of graphs to allow the pilot to calculate the expected performance of the aircraft for different flight phases. The most commonly used graphs are those for take-off and landing performance, and those are the ones we will concentrate on here. However the same principles can be used on the other graphs. Two things to remember: Firstly the chart performance is obtained by using the recommended techniques – to get graph results follow chart procedures. Secondly you can safely assume that the graph results have been obtained by placing a brand new aircraft in the hands of an experienced test pilot under favourable conditions. To make allowances for a less than new aircraft, being flown by an average mortal in the real conditions it is wise to 'factor' any results you get. The charts may be 'factored' to make allowances for the real world, and if so the chart will be annotated as such. If not some form of safety factoring is highly recommended. Public transport operations are subject to overall factoring of 1.33 for take-offs and 1.43 for landings, this figure being incorporated in the relevant graphs. It is highly recommended that the pilot apply the same factor to any graph figures ie a calculated take-off distance of 500 meters becomes 500 x 1.33 = 665 meters. As with loading calculations the pilot must use the graphs and data from the documents for the individual aircraft being used. The graphs and diagrams used in this section are for illustrative purposes only, and not for operational use.

In the next section conversion factors between feet and metres are listed, together with recommended factors for variations not necessarily covered by the flight manual graphs.

▶ PA-28 Warrior Takeoff and Landing Performance Graphs

The takeoff distance and landing distance graphs in the flight manual make several assumptions; (paved, level, dry, runway; use of flight manual technique). Different graphs are provided for different flap settings for take-off.

The graphs use the term "Pressure Altitude". This is the altitude of the runway assuming a standard pressure setting (ie 1013mb – or 1013 hectopascal if you prefer). On a day with a QNH other than 1013 you will need to adjust the actual altitude to get the pressure altitude. For instance on a day with a QNH above 1013 the pressure altitude will be less than the actual, and vica versa. To do this conversion, simply adjust the actual altitude by 30ft for each millibar/hectopascal above or below 1013.

The headwind or tailwind component is calculated from the windspeed and the angle to the runway (ie a 10 knot wind directly down the runway gives a headwind component of 10 knots. A 10 knot wind at 90° to the runway gives a headwind component of 0). There is a graph in section 7 for calculating head/tail wind component and crosswind component.

The take-off distance & landing distance graphs will state the technique used to obtain the figures. Remember, to get graph results you have to use the graph techniques.

▶Take-off Performance

The take-off performance can be divided into two sections:

The TAKE-OFF RUN (or Take-Off Ground Roll), the distance taken for the aircraft to become airborne, and;

The TAKE-OFF DISTANCE, that is the total distance required for the aircraft to become airborne AND clear a 50' barrier

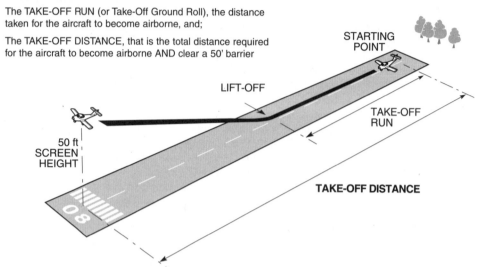

▶Take-off Distance Calculation Example

For this example we will take the conditions as:

Outside Air Temperature	+10°
Pressure Altitude	1200ft
take-off weight	2200lbs
Headwind Component	5 Knots

Start at the temperature +10°C, and then go vertically to the pressure altitude of 1200 feet, now go horizontally to the REFERENCE LINE, then proceed parallel to the guideline until above the 2200lbs point. From this point take a line horizontally to the next reference line and then follow the guide line until above the 5kts point. Take a line horizontally to the far side of the graph and read of the take of distance of 1500 feet. This figure is then multiplied by the safety factor of 1.33 to give 1995 feet.

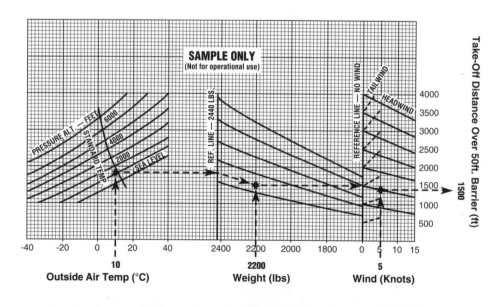

▶ Landing Performance

The landing performance is calculated as the LANDING DISTANCE, that is the total distance from 50' over the runway to a full stop. The ground roll (or ground run) – the distance from touch down to full stop may also be calculated

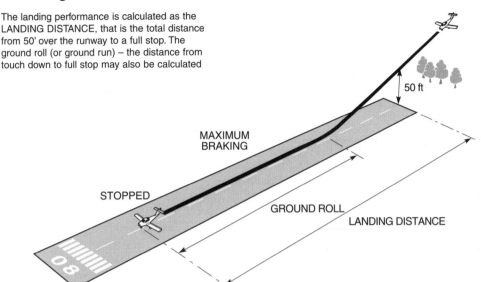

▶ Landing Distance Calculation Example

For this example we will take the conditions as:

Outside Air Temperature	+16°C
Pressure Altitude	1000ft
Landing weight	2100lbs
Headwind Component	nil wind

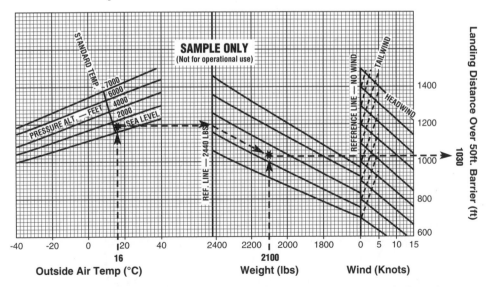

On the landing distance graph again start at the temperature (+16°C) and go vertically to the pressure altitude (1000ft). From this point go horizontally to the REFERENCE LINE, and then along the guideline until above the 2100lbs point. Then go horizontally to the wind reference line. As there is nil wind carry on horizontally to the far side of the graph and read off the landing distance in feet – 1030ft. If this figure is factored by 1.43 you get the result of 1473ft.

▶Enroute Performance

Data is also provided in the flight manual for calculating the enroute performance, such as range and endurance. It should be noted that the figures obtained in these charts rely on the use of the quoted procedures, particularly the leaning procedure. If any other procedure is used the quoted performance is unlikely to be achieved.

PA-28 Warrior Take-Off Distance
Paved Level Dry Runway, Flaps 25°

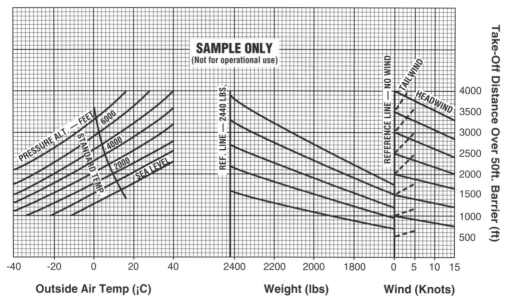

PA-28 Warrior Landing Distance
Paved Level Dry Runway, Flaps 40°

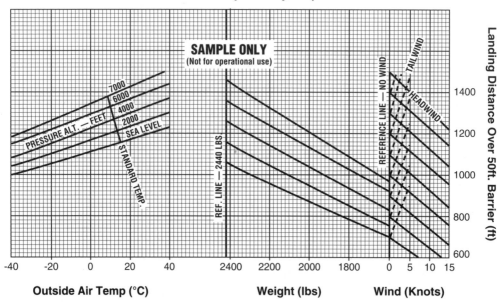

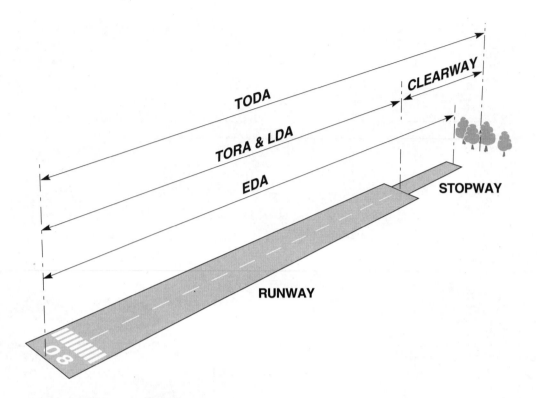

▶Runway Dimensions

Having calculated the distances the aircraft requires for take-off or landing, the runway dimensions must be checked to ensure that the aircraft can be safely operated on the runway in question. The figures given in the AIP or airfield guide can be defined in a number of ways.

The Take-off Run Available (TORA)

The TORA is the length of the runway available for the take-off ground run of the aircraft. This is usually the physical length of the runway.

The Emergency Distance Available (EDA)

The EDA is the length of the TORA plus the length of any stopway. A stopway is an area at the end of the TORA prepared for an aircraft to stop on in the event of an abandoned take-off. The ED is also known as the

ACCELERATE – STOP DISTANCE AVAILABLE.

The Take-off Distance Available (TODA)

The TODA is the TORA plus the length of any clearway. A clearway is an area over which an aircraft may make its initial climb (to 50' in this instance). The TODA will not be more than 1.5 x TORA.

The Landing Distance Available (LDA)

The LDA is the length of the runway available for the ground run of an aircraft landing.

Conversions

Conversions

▶ Take-off Distance Factors

▶ Landing Distance Factors

▶ Runway Contamination

▶ Use of the Wind Component Graph

▶ Wind Component Graph

▶ Temperature and Pressure

▶ Metric/Imperial Measurement

▶ Distance – Metres/Feet

▶ Distance – Km/nm/sm

▶ Weight – lbs/Kg

▶ Volume – Fluid

▶ Millibars/Inches

▶Take-off Distance Factors

The following factors will allow the pilot to make allowance for variations that may effect take-off performance. Although some of these factors are covered in the PA-28 Warrior performance graphs, the table is produced in its entirety for completeness:

VARIATION	INCREASE IN TAKE-OFF DISTANCE (to 50')	FACTOR
10% increase in aircraft weight	20%	1.2
Increase of 1000' in runway altitude	10%	1.1
Increase in temperature of 10°C	10%	1.1
Dry Grass		
– Short (under 5 inches)	20%	1.2
– Long (5-10 inches)	25%	1.25
Wet Grass		
–Short	25%	1.25
–Long	30%	1.3
2% uphill slope	10%	1.1
Tailwind component of		
10% of lift off speed	20%	1.2
Soft ground or snow *	at least 25%	at least 1.25

The following factors will allow the pilot to make allowance for variations that may affect take-off performance. Although some of these factors are covered in the Warrior performance graphs, the table is produced in its entirety for completeness:

* snow and other runway contamination is covered on page 86.

▶Landing Distance Factors

The following factors will allow the pilot to make allowance for variations that may effect landing performance. Although some of these factors are covered in the PA-28 Warrior performance graphs, the table is produced in its entirety for completeness:

VARIATION	INCREASE IN TAKE-OFF DISTANCE (to 50')	FACTOR
10% increase in aircraft weight	10%	1.1
Increase of 1000' in runway altitude	5%	1.05
Increase in temperature of 10°C	5%	1.05
Dry Grass		
– Short (under 5 inches)	20%	1.2
– Long (5-10 inches)	30%	1.3
Wet Grass		
– Short	30%	1.30
– Long	40%	1.40
2% downhill slope	10%	1.1
Tailwind component of 10% of landing speed	20%	1.2
snow*	at least 25%	at least 1.25

* snow and other runway contamination is covered on page 86.

▶Runway Contamination

A runway can be contaminated by water, snow or slush. If operation on such a runway cannot be avoided additional allowance must be made for the problems such contamination may cause – ie additional drag, reduced braking performance (possible aquaplaning), and directional control problems.

It is generally recommended that take-off should not be attempted if dry snow covers the runway to a depth of more than 60mm, or if water, slush or wet snow covers the runway to more than 15mm. In addition a tailwind, or crosswind component exceeding 10 knots, should not be accepted when operating on a slippery runway.

For take-off distance required calculations the other known conditions should be factored, and the emergency distance available on the runway should be at least 2.0 X the take-off distance required (for a paved runway) or at least 2.66 X the take-off distance required (for a grass runway).

When landing any water or slush can have a very adverse effect on landing performance, and the danger of aquaplaning (with negligible wheel braking and loss of directional control) is very real.

▶ Use of the Wind Component Graph

This graph can be used to find the head/tail wind component and the crosswind component, given a particular wind velocity and runway direction.

EXAMPLE:

>   Runway 27

>   Surface wind 240°/15 knots

The angle between the runway direction (270°) and wind direction (240°) is 30°. Now on the graph locate a point on the 30° line, where it crosses the 15 knot arc. From this point take a horizontal line to give the headwind component (13 knots) and a vertical line to give the crosswind component (8 knots).

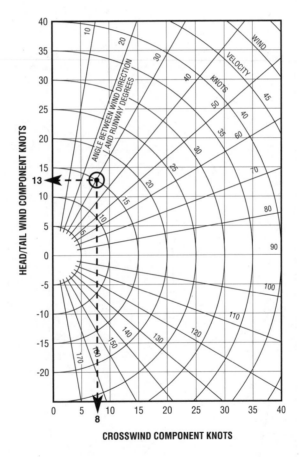

On the main graph overleaf the shaded area represents the crosswind limit for this aircraft. If the wind point is within this shaded area, the crosswind limit for this aircraft has been exceeded.

>   Note: Runway direction will be degrees magnetic. Check the wind direction given is also in degrees magnetic.

Wind Component Graph

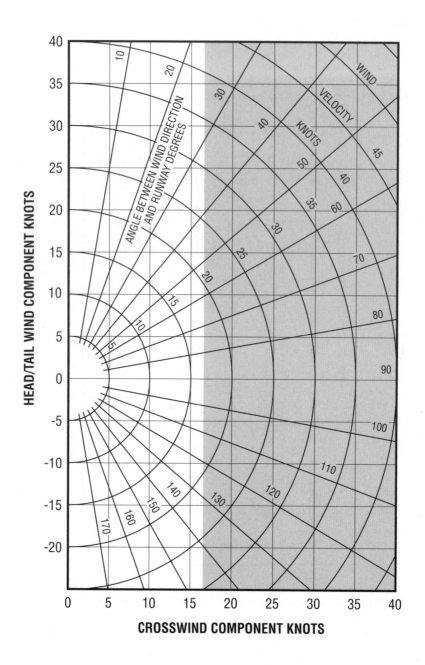

Temperature & Pressure

Metric/Imperial Measurement

Metres	Feet	Feet	Metres
1	3.28	1	0.30
2	6.56	2	0.61
3	9.84	3	0.91
4	13.12	4	1.22
5	16.40	5	1.52
6	19.69	6	1.83
7	22.97	7	2.13
8	26.25	8	2.44
9	29.53	9	2.74
10	32.81	10	3.05
20	65.62	20	6.10
30	98.43	30	9.14
40	131.23	40	12.19
50	164.04	50	15.24
60	196.85	60	18.29
70	229.66	70	21.34
80	262.47	80	24.38
90	295.28	90	27.43
100	328.08	100	30.48
200	656.16	200	60.96
300	984.25	300	91.44
400	1,312.34	400	121.92
500	1,640.42	500	152.40
600	1,968.50	600	182.88
700	2,296.59	700	213.36
800	2,624.67	800	243.84
900	2,952.76	900	274.32
1000	3,280.84	1000	304.80
2000	6,561.70	2000	609.60
3000	9,842.50	3000	914.40
4000	13,123.40	4000	1,219.20
5000	16,404.20	5000	1,524.00
6000	19,685.00	6000	1,828.80
7000	22,965.90	7000	2,133.60
8000	26,246.70	8000	2,438.40
9000	29,527.60	9000	2,743.20
10000	32,808.40	10000	3,048.00

Km/Nautical Miles/Statute Miles

nm	Km	St	Km	nm	St
1	1.85	1.15	1	.54	.62
2	3.70	2.30	2	1.08	1.24
3	5.56	3.45	3	1.62	1.86
4	7.41	4.60	4	2.16	2.49
5	9.26	5.75	5	2.70	3.11
6	11.11	6.90	6	3.24	3.73
7	12.96	8.06	7	3.78	4.35
8	14.82	9.21	8	4.32	4.97
9	16.67	10.36	9	4.86	5.59
10	18.52	11.51	10	5.40	6.21
20	37.04	23.02	20	10.80	12.43
30	55.56	34.52	30	16.20	18.64
40	74.08	46.03	40	21.60	24.86
50	92.60	57.54	50	27.00	31.07
60	111.12	69.05	60	32.40	37.28
70	129.64	80.55	70	37.80	43.50
80	148.16	92.06	80	43.20	49.71
90	166.68	103.57	90	48.60	55.92
100	185.2	115.1	100	54.0	62.1
200	370.4	230.2	200	108.0	124.3
300	555.6	345.2	300	162.0	186.4
400	740.8	460.3	400	216.0	248.6
500	926.0	575.4	500	270.0	310.7
600	1111.2	690.5	600	324.0	372.8
700	1296.4	805.6	700	378.0	435.0
800	1481.6	920.6	800	432.0	497.1
900	1666.8	1035.7	900	486.0	559.2

Conversion Factors:

Centimetres to Inches x .3937
Inches to Centimetres x 2.54
Metres to Feet x 3.28084
Feet to Metres x 0.3048

Statute Miles to Nautical Miles x 0.868976
Statute Miles to Kilometres x 1.60934
Kilometres to Statute Miles x 0.62137
Kilometres to Nautical Miles x 0.539957
Nautical Miles to Statute Miles x 1.15078
Nautical Miles to Kilometres x 1.852

Km/Nautical Miles/Statute Miles

ST	nm	Km
1	.87	1.61
2	1.74	3.22
3	2.61	4.83
4	3.48	6.44
5	4.34	8.05
6	5.21	9.66
7	6.08	11.27
8	6.95	12.87
9	7.82	14.48
10	8.69	16.09
20	17.38	32.19
30	26.07	48.28
40	34.76	64.37
50	43.45	80.47
60	52.14	96.56
70	60.83	112.65
80	69.52	128.75
90	78.21	144.84
100	86.9	161.0
200	173.8	321.9
300	260.7	482.8
400	347.6	643.7
500	434.5	804.7
600	521.4	965.6
700	608.3	1126.5
800	695.2	1287.5
900	782.1	1448.4

Conversion Factors:

lbs to Kilograms x 0.45359
Kilograms to lbs x 2.20462

Weight lbs/Kg

lbs	Kg	Kg	lbs
1	.45	1	2.20
2	.91	2	4.41
3	1.38	3	6.61
4	1.81	4	8.82
5	2.27	5	11.02
6	2.72	6	13.23
7	3.18	7	15.43
8	3.63	8	17.64
9	4.08	9	19.84
10	4.54	10	22.05
20	9.07	20	44.09
30	13.61	30	66.14
40	18.14	40	88.18
50	22.68	50	110.23
60	27.22	60	132.28
70	31.75	70	154.32
80	36.29	80	176.37
90	40.82	90	198.42
100	45.4	100	220.5
200	90.7	200	440.9
300	136.1	300	661.4
400	181.4	400	881.8
500	226.8	500	1102.3
600	272.2	600	1322.8
700	317.5	700	1543.2
800	362.9	800	1763.7
900	408.2	900	1984.2
1000	453.6	1000	2204.6
2000	907.2	2000	4409.2
3000	1360.8	3000	6613.9
4000	1814.4	4000	8818.5
5000	2268.0	5000	11023.1
6000	2721.5	6000	13227.7
7000	3175.1	7000	15432.3
8000	3628.7	8000	17637.0
9000	4082.3	9000	19841.6
10000	4535.9	10000	22046.2

Volume (Fluid)

Litres	Imp Gall	U.S. Gall
1	0.22	0.26
2	0.44	0.53
3	0.66	0.79
4	0.88	1.06
5	1.10	1.32
6	1.32	1.59
7	1.54	1.85
8	1.76	2.11
9	1.98	2.38
10	2.20	2.64
20	4.40	5.28
30	6.60	7.93
40	8.80	10.57
50	11.00	13.21
60	13.20	15.85
70	15.40	18.49
80	17.60	21.14
90	19.80	23.78
100	22.00	26.42
200	44.00	52.84
300	66.00	79.26
400	88.00	105.68
500	110.00	132.10
600	132.00	158.52
700	154.00	184.94
800	176.00	211.36
900	198.00	237.78
1000	220.00	264.20

U.S Gall	Imp Gall	Litres	Imp Gall	U.S. Gall	Litres
1	0.83	3.79	1	1.20	4.55
2	1.67	7.57	2	2.40	9.09
3	2.50	11.36	3	3.60	13.64
4	3.33	15.14	4	4.80	18.18
5	4.16	18.93	5	6.00	22.73
6	5.00	22.71	6	7.21	27.28
7	5.83	26.50	7	8.41	31.82
8	6.66	30.28	8	9.61	36.37
9	7.49	34.07	9	10.81	40.91
10	8.33	37.85	10	12.01	45.46
20	16.65	75.71	20	24.02	90.92
30	24.98	113.56	30	36.03	136.38
40	33.31	151.41	40	48.04	181.84
50	41.63	189.27	50	60.05	227.30
60	49.96	227.12	60	72.06	272.76
70	58.29	264.97	70	84.07	318.22
80	66.61	302.82	80	96.08	363.68
90	74.94	340.68	90	108.09	409.14
100	83.27	378.54	100	120.09	454.60

Conversion Factors:

Imperial Gallons to Litres x 4.54596
Litres to Imperial Gallons x 0.219975
U.S. Gallons to Litres x 3.78541
Litres to U.S. Gallons x 0.264179
Imperial Gallons to U.S. Gallons x 1.20095
U.S. Gallons to Imperial Gallons x 0.832674

Millibars/Inches

Mbs	ins	Mbs	ins	Mbs	ins	Mbs	ins
950	28.054	980	28.939	1010	29.825	1040	30.711
951	28.083	981	28.969	1011	29.855	1041	30.741
952	28.113	982	28.998	1012	29.884	1042	30.770
953	28.142	983	29.028	1013	29.914	1043	30.800
954	28.172	984	29.058	1014	29.943	1044	30.829
955	28.201	985	29.087	1015	29.973	1045	30.859
956	28.231	986	29.117	1016	30.002	1046	30.888
957	28.260	987	29.146	1017	30.032	1047	30.918
958	28.290	988	29.176	1018	30.062	1048	30.947
959	28.319	989	29.205	1019	30.091	1049	30.977
960	28.349	990	29.235	1020	30.121	1050	31.007
961	28.378	991	29.264	1021	30.150		
962	28.408	992	29.294	1022	30.180		
963	28.437	993	29.323	1023	30.209		
964	28.467	994	29.353	1024	30.239		
965	28.496	995	29.382	1025	30.268		
966	28.526	996	29.412	1026	30.298		
967	28.556	997	29.441	1027	30.327		
968	28.585	998	29.471	1028	30.357		
969	28.615	999	29.500	1029	30.386		
970	28.644	1000	29.530	1030	30.416		
971	28.674	1001	29.560	1031	30.445		
972	28.703	1002	29.589	1032	30.475		
973	28.733	1003	29.619	1033	30.504		
974	28.762	1004	29.648	1034	30.534		
975	28.792	1005	29.678	1035	30.564		
976	28.821	1006	29.707	1036	30.593		
977	28.851	1007	29.737	1037	30.623		
978	28.880	1008	29.766	1038	30.652		
979	28.910	1009	29.796	1039	30.682		

To convert Inches into millibars multiply by 33.86
To convert millibars into Inches multiply by 0.0295

Index

Index